The Journal of the International Society for
Oncodevelopmental Biology and Medicine (ISOBM)

TumorBiology

Tumor Markers, Tumor Targeting and Translational Cancer Research

Founded 1980 as 'Oncodevelopmental Biology and Medicine' by the ISOBM, continued 1984–1986 as 'Tumour Biology'. Former Editors: W.H. Fishman 1980–1983, H. Hirai 1980–1993, A.M. Neville 1984–1994, S. von Kleist 1995–1999.

KARGER

Printed in Switzerland on acid-free paper by Reinhardt Druck, Basel

Appears bimonthly: 1 volume per year (6 issues)

Tumor Biology

Guidelines for Authors

Introduction

Tumor Biology is an international journal publishing original research and reviews in experimental and clinical cancer research. Translational research with a focus on tumor markers and tumor targeting are major interests, but studies in other areas of basic or clinical cancer research are also welcome. Manuscript categories include Research Articles, Reviews, Workshop Reports, Editorials, and Research Commentaries.

Submission

Only original papers written in English are considered and should be submitted **online.** For specific instructions on how to prepare a manuscript for submission, you are encouraged to view the guidelines at **www.karger.com/tbi**, where you will also find a link to the **Submission Website**. Should you have any problems with your submission or feel the need to submit the paper in a non-electronic form, please contact the editorial office:

Dr. Phil D. Rye
Managing Editor Tumor Biology
Tel. +47 22 70 07 66
Fax +47 22 70 07 70
E-mail phil.rye@no.axis-shield.com

Reviews: Review articles are usually by invitation only. However, proposals clearly outlining a theme including a probable submission date are welcome. Suggestions for articles can be submitted by e-mail to the Editor-in-Chief:

Prof. Torgny Stigbrand
torgny.stigbrand@climi.umu.se

Research commentaries: Research commentaries are usually initiated by the editorial board, although unsolicited submissions are welcome. Prospective authors should contact the Managing Editor (phil.rye@no.axis-shield.com).

Conditions

All manuscripts are subject to peer review. Manuscripts are received with the explicit understanding that they are not under simultaneous consideration by any other publication. A cover letter with the name, address, and telephone and fax numbers of the corresponding author must accompany each manuscript. This letter must include a statement that affirms that all authors agree with the submission. Submission of an article for publication implies transfer of the copyright from the author to the publisher upon acceptance. Accepted papers become the permanent property of *Tumor Biology* and may not be reproduced by any means, in whole or in part, without the written consent of the publisher and the Editor-in-Chief. It is the author's responsibility to obtain permission to reproduce illustrations, tables, etc. from other publications.

Arrangement

The complete manuscript (including table legends, figure legends and references) should be typed double-spaced using a 12 point font on one side of the paper (A4 size or 8½ × 11 inches) with 2.5 cm (1 inch) margins on all sides and with page numbers. Articles should contain: Title page, Key Words, Abstract, Introduction, Materials and Methods, Results, Discussion, Acknowledgements, References, Tables and figure legends.

Title page: The first page of each paper should indicate the title, the authors' names, the institute where the work was conducted, and a short title for use as running head.
NB: Authors wishing to preserve the phonetic meaning of diacritics (PubMed reduces diacritics to their root characters) must spell their names accordingly when submitting manuscripts (e.g. Müller should be Mueller).

Full address: The exact postal address of the corresponding author complete with postal code must be given at the bottom of the title page. Please also supply phone and fax numbers, as well as e-mail address.

Key words: For indexing purposes, a list of 3–10 key words in English is essential.

Abstract: Each paper requires an abstract of up to 200 words clearly outlining the objective(s), methods, results, and conclusion(s).

Footnotes: Avoid footnotes.

Tables and illustrations: Tables and illustrations (both numbered in Arabic numerals) should be prepared on separate pages. Tables require a heading and figures a legend, also prepared on a separate page. For the reproduction of illustrations, only good drawings and original photographs can be accepted; negatives or photocopies cannot be used. Due to technical reasons, figures with a screen background should not be submitted. When possible, group several illustrations in one block for reproduction (max. size 180 × 223 mm) or provide crop marks. On the back of each illustration, indicate its number, the author's name, and 'top' with a soft pencil. Electronically submitted b/w half-tone and color illustrations must have a final resolution of 300 dpi after scaling, line drawings one of 800–1,200 dpi.

Color illustrations: Up to 6 color illustrations per page can be integrated within the text at the special price of CHF/USD 660.00 per page. Color illustrations are reproduced at the author's expense.

References: In the text identify references by Arabic numerals [in square brackets]. The number of references should not normally exceed 40 for Research Articles, and 80 for Reviews. Material submitted for publication but not yet accepted should be noted as 'unpublished data' and not be included in the reference list. The list of references should include only those publications which are cited in the text. Do not alphabetize; number references in the order in which they are first mentioned in the text. The surnames of the authors followed by initials should be given. There should be no punctuation other than a comma to separate the authors. Preferably, please cite all authors. Abbreviate journal names according to the Index Medicus system. (Also see International Committee of Medical Journal Editors: Uniform requirements for manuscripts submitted to biomedical journals. N Engl J Med 1997;336:309-315. www.icmje.org)

Digital Object Identifier (DOI)
S. Karger Publishers supports DOIs as unique identifiers for articles. A DOI number will be printed on the title page of each article. DOIs can be useful in the future for identifying and citing articles published online without volume or issue information. More information can be found at www.doi.org.

Examples
(a) Papers published in periodicals: Sun J, Koto H, Chung KF: Interaction of ozone and allergen challenges on bronchial responsiveness and inflammation in sensitised guinea pigs. Int Arch Allergy Immunol 1997;112:191–195.
(b) Papers published only with DOI numbers: Theoharides TC, Boucher W, Spear K: Serum interleukin-6 reflects disease severity and osteoporosis in mastocytosis patients. Int Arch Allergy Immunol DOI: 10.1159/000063858.
(c) Monographs: Matthews DE, Farewell VT: Using and Understanding Medical Statistics, ed 3, revised. Basel, Karger, 1996.
(d) Edited books: Parren PWHI, Burton DR: Antibodies against HIV-1 from phage display libraries: Mapping of an immune response and progress towards antiviral immunotherapy; in Capra JD (ed): Antibody Engineering. Chem Immunol. Basel, Karger, 1997, vol 65, pp 18–56.

Page Charges

There are no page charges for articles of 3 (ISOBM members and *Tumor Biology* subscribers: 5) or fewer printed pages (including tables, illustrations and references). Each additional complete or partial page is charged to the author at CHF/USD 240.00. One printed page is equal to approximately 3 manuscript pages (including tables, illustrations and references).

Proofs

Unless otherwise indicated, proofs are sent to the first-named author and should be returned with the least possible delay. Alterations made in proofs, other than the correction of printer's errors, are charged to the author. No page proofs are supplied.

Reprints

Order forms and a price list are sent with the proofs. Orders submitted after the issue is printed are subject to considerably higher prices.

KARGER

Fax +41 61 306 12 34
E-Mail karger@karger.ch
www.karger.com

The Guidelines for Authors are available at:
www.karger.com/tbi_Guidelines

TumorBiology

General Information

Publication data: 'Tumor Biology' is published 6 times a year. Volume 27 with 6 issues appears in 2006.

Subscription rates: Subscriptions run for a full calendar year. Prices are given per year.
Personal subscription:

Print or Online	Print/Online combined
CHF 609.50	CHF 654.50
EUR 451.50	EUR 484.50
USD 554.00	USD 595.00
postage and handling	(added to print and print/online)
CHF 33.60 Europe,	CHF 49.80 Overseas
EUR 24.30	
USD 45.60	

Institutional subscription:

Print or Online	Print/Online combined
CHF 1219.00	CHF 1317.00
EUR 903.00	EUR 976.00
USD 1108.00	USD 1197.00
postage and handling	(added to print and print/online)
CHF 42.00 Europe,	CHF 62.40 Overseas
EUR 30.30	
USD 57.00	

Airmail surcharge: CHF 42.00 / USD 38.10
Discount subscription prices: American Association for Cancer Research; European Association for Cancer Research; Japanese Cancer Association. Tumor Biology is included in 'International Society for Oncodevelopmental Biology and Medicine (ISOBM)' membership fee, for information: http://www.med.uio.no/isobm

Microforms: Please direct all enquiries and orders to:
University Microfilms Inc.
300 North Zeeb Road, P.O. Box 1346
Ann Arbor, MI 48106-1346 (USA)

Subscription orders: Orders can be placed at agencies, bookstores, directly with the Publisher
S. Karger AG, P.O. Box
CH–4009 Basel (Switzerland)
or with any of the following distributors:
Deutschland: S. Karger GmbH, Postfach
D–79095 Freiburg
France: Librairie Luginbühl
36, bd de Latour-Maubourg
F–75007 Paris
Great Britain, Ireland: S. Karger AG
4 Rickett Street
London SW6 1RU, UK
USA: S. Karger Publishers, Inc.
26 West Avon Road, P.O. Box 529
Farmington, CT 06085, USA
India, Bangladesh, Sri Lanka:
Panther Publishers Private Ltd.
33, First Main
Koramangala First Block
Bangalore 560 034, India
Japan: Karger Japan, Inc.
Yushima S Bld. 3F
4-2-3, Yushima, Bunkyo-ku
Tokyo 113-0034, Japan

Change of address: Both old and new address should be sent to the subscription source.

Single issues and back volumes: Information can be obtained through the Publisher.

Advertising: Correspondence and rate requests should be addressed to the Publisher.

Bibliographic indices: This journal is regularly listed in bibliographic services, including *Current Contents*® and Index Medicus/MEDLINE.

Book Reviews: Books are accepted for review by special agreement.

Copying: This journal has been registered with the Copyright Clearance Center (CCC), as indicated by the code appearing on the first page of each article. For readers in the US, this code signals consent for copying of articles for personal or internal use, or for the personal or internal use of specific clients, provided that the stated fee is paid per copy directly to
Copyright Clearance Center Inc.
222 Rosewood Drive
Danvers, MA 01923 (USA)
A copy of the first page of the article must accompany payment. Consent does not extend to copying for general distribution, for promotion, for creating new works, or for resale. In these cases, specific written permission must be obtained from the copyright owner,
S. Karger AG,
P.O. Box, CH–4009 Basel (Switzerland)

Disk Submission

A **comprehensive version** of these guidelines for the **submission of manuscripts and illustrations on disk** can be accessed online under **www.karger.com/disksubmission** or requested as a leaflet from the editorial department.

Please follow the general rules on style and arrangement in the **'Guidelines for Authors'** of the journal. Submit a **double-spaced printout** of your manuscript matching the file on disk exactly.

Technical Information

Store only data pertinent to this manuscript. Include your fonts (screen and printer fonts for Macintosh). For a **text only** manuscript, use a 3.5-inch disk. For **text and illustrations,** use 3.5 or 5.25 Magneto Optical Disc; CD-ROM (DOS or hybrid); iomega Zip/DOS (100 MB), or 44 MB, 88 MB or 200 MB SyQuest. Compress extensive data using ZIP format.

Data Description

Label your disk with the **title of the journal or book** for which it is submitted; a **short version** of the paper's title; your **name,** postal and e-mail address, fax and phone number; **hard- and software** used, including the version; and the **complete list of the file names.** File names consist of eight characters before the dot identifying the file and three characters after the dot identifying the application.

Text and Format

The **preferred word-processing package is MS-Word.** Other commonly used PC text programs and ASCII formats are accepted.
Update your data when you revise subsequent to the reviewer's or editor's decision and mark revisions clearly. Manuscripts accepted for publication are subject to **copy editing:** changes and/or questions will be marked in the manuscript, which will be returned to you with your disk and the galley proofs for checking.
Enter your text continuously flush left. Do not use any layout functions. Do not split words at the end of a line. **Do not use indentations.** Use a blank line before and a hard return at the end of paragraphs.
Arrange headings flush left. Insert only **one space after punctuation marks.** Insert Greek letters, mathematical symbols etc. with your word-processing program. Use **boldface and italics** as well as sub- and superscript where appropriate.
Tables are part of the text and should be placed at the end of the text file. Separate the individual parts of a table by lines. Use the tabulator instead of spaces. Format operation data on one line in the same column.

Legends to illustrations are part of the text and should also be listed at the end of the text file.

Illustrations

Store illustrations as separate files: do not integrate them in your text. Export **line drawings/vector graphics** as TIF, EPS or WMF format. Use Photoshop for processing and retouching **scanned half-tone images.** Save the original scan and the processed version. Export **black and white or color images** as TIF or EPS format in their anticipated size in print. **For detailed information** on how to submit illustration data on disk please consult the leaflet or **www.karger.com/disksubmission.**

KI 02 DISK

KARGER

Fax +41 61 306 12 34
E-Mail karger@karger.ch
www.karger.com

The Journal Home Page is available at:
www.karger.com/tbi

Tumor Biology

Cancer Research, Tumor Markers, Clinical Oncology

Abstracts

The XXXIIIrd Meeting of the International Society for Oncodevelopmental Biology and Medicine, ISOBM 2005

September 24–28, 2005, Rhodes, Greece

Organizer

V. Barak, Jerusalem, Israel

KARGER

Basel · Freiburg · Paris · London · New York ·
Bangalore · Bangkok · Singapore · Tokyo · Sydney

The organizers would also like to acknowledge the following sponsors for their support of the ISOBM 2005 meeting

ABBOTT Diagnostics
ROCHE Diagnostics GmbH
BECKMAN COULTER Inc.
DIASORIN
DPC
CIS BioInternational
BRAHMS
PERKIN ELMER
CANAG Diagnostics
GEN-PROBE Inc.
WHATMAN-SCHLEICHER & SCHUELL
PRO-PHARMACEUTICALS Inc.
IMCLONE SYSTEMS Inc.
IDL Biotech AB
MEDAC GmbH

S. Karger
Medical and Scientific Publishers
Basel • Freiburg • Paris • London
New York • Bangalore • Bangkok
Singapore • Tokyo • Sydney

Printed in Germany by Miraprint Copy & Druck, Gauting
ISBN 3–8055–8023–1

KARGER

Fax +41 61 306 12 34
E-Mail karger@karger.ch
www.karger.com

Key Notes - 1

Abstract not submitted.

Key Notes - 2

Amplification of p53 induced "SIGNATURE GENES" in cells transformed in vitro

Rotter Varda[1], Milyavsky M[1], Tabach Y[1,2], Shats I[1], Erez N[1], Cohen Y[1], Tang X[1], Kalis M[1], Buganim Y[1], Goldfinger N[1], Ginsberg D[1], Domany E[2],Pilpel Y[3]
[1]Department of Molecular Cell Biology, [2]Department of Physics of Complex Systems, [3]Department of Molecular Genetics, Weizmann Institute of Science, Rehovot , Israel.

It is well accepted that inactivation of p53 plays a pivotal role in malignant transformation of cells. However, the networks of transcription programs that are modulated following p53 inactivation are still unknown. To decipher these, we subjected hTERT immortalized cells that were gradually transformed *in vitro* by p53 inactivation in conjunction with other oncogenic stress signals such as loss of the INK4A locus and *ras* over expression, to an extensive bioinformatics analysis. A genome wide expression profiling identified distinct genetic signatures corresponding to the genetic alterations listed above. Most importantly, unique cellular phenotypes, such as differentiation block, aberrant mitotic progression, increased angiogenesis and invasiveness were identified and coupled with genetic signatures assigned for the genetic alterations in the p53, INK4A locus, and H-Ras respectively. Furthermore, a transcriptional program that defines the cellular response to p53 inactivation was an excellent predictor of metastasis development and bad prognosis in breast cancer patients. Deciphering universal transcriptional programs, which are affected by the most common oncogenic mutations, provides considerable insight into regulatory circuits controlling malignant transformation and will, hopefully, open new avenues for rational therapeutic decisions.

Key Notes - 3

HER 2 and EGFR: signaling mechanisms and targets for anti-cancer therapies

Yarden Yosef
Department of Biological Regulation, The Weizmann Institute of Science, Rehovot 76100, Israel

Growth factors and their transmembrane receptor tyrosine kinases regulate cellular proliferation and migration during both embryogenesis and oncogenesis. An example is the ErbB family of receptors. Several mechanisms underlie the involvement of ErbB proteins and their EGF-like ligands in human cancer. One mechanism involves autocrine loops comprising co-expression of a receptor and the respective ligands. Another mechanism entails genetic aberrations, which affect primarily ErbB-1 (also called EGFR). These alterations involve large deletions of extracellular as well as intracellular domains and they are frequently observed in brain tumors. Likewise, short deletions or point mutations confined to the kinase domain have recently been reported in lung cancer. Last, overexpression of EGFR or ErbB-2/HER2 in human carcinomas characterizes a relatively aggressive subset of head and neck (EGFR) and mammary (HER2) tumors. Several therapeutic strategies target ErbB signaling. The most successful is the utilization of humanized monoclonal antibodies to ErbB-2/HER2 or to EGFR/ErbB-1. Another approach entails the use of low molecular weight antagonists of the tyrosine kinase domain shared by all four ErbB proteins. Finally, disrupting Hsp90-HER2 interactions leads to effective degradation of HER2/ErbB-2 in proteasomes, and constitutes another strategy to block ErbB-2/HER2-driven tumors. The underlying biochemical mechanisms and initial clinical lessons will be discussed.

Key Notes - 4

Lynch syndrome and hereditary diffuse gastric cancer as models for cancer education and prevention

Lynch Henry, Jansen M, Lynch JF, Gong G., Deters CA
Department of Preventive Medicine/Public Health, Creighton University, Omaha, Nebraska, Huntsman, D.British Columbia Cancer Agency, Vancouver, B.C.

Aims: We aim to show that screening is effective in preventing colon cancer in mutation carriers with the Lynch syndrome, while in contrast, screening is often ineffective in detecting early gastric cancer in persons with hereditary diffuse gastric cancer (HDGC). However, prophylactic total gastrectomy may be lifesaving for carriers of the CDH1 mutation, also known as the E-cadherin gene in HDGC. Knowledge about these facts in the genetic counseling setting is mandatory.

Methods: The study of any hereditary cancer syndrome family includes intensive genealogy ascertainment, with painstaking review of medical and pathology documents so that cancer diagnoses can, whenever possible, be confirmed. Genetic counseling is provided followed by DNA testing, when available. Family members, once educated about the cancer syndrome, can be highly effective volunteer teachers of those high risk relatives whom we have not been able to contact.

Results: Our experience with educating patients and physicians, including recommended cancer control measures such as screening and surgical prophylaxis, will be discussed. For example, nine members of an HDGC family with CDH1 mutation underwent prophylactic total gastrectomy.

Conclusions: Physicians often may not recognize patients' hereditary risk for cancer; therefore, this limits the potential for cancer control. Proper diagnosis of a hereditary cancer syndrome, combined with appropriate screening, and in certain syndromes, surgical prophylaxis could be lifesaving.

Key Notes - 5

Carcinoembryonic Antign (CEA) 1965-2005

Gold Phil
Departments of Medicine, Physiology and Oncology, McGill University and Health Centre, Canada

Forty (40) years have passed since the initial publication dealing with the description of the carcinoembryonic antigen (CEA). The review will deal with the initial discovery of the molecule, and the purification and characterization of CEA. The description of the radioimmunoassay for this tumour-related material initiated a great deal of activity in evaluating the role of CEA in cancer diagnosis, and radioimmunolocalization. Subsequent studies led to the cellular localization of CEA and its distribution in both normal and tumour tissues. A 'CEA family' of molecules (the CEACAMs) has been described, and the genes for both CEA, and many of its relatives, have been cloned. More recently, there have been a number of approaches taken to the use of CEA in human cancer therapy. The results of a number of these studies have very promising vis-vis cancer patient treatment.

These have been exciting times for biomedical research, from which studies of CEA have benefited greatly. The work described above will be reviewed, briefly, and the role of the ISOBM and, most particularly, of it members, will be discussed.

Key Notes - 6

Regulation and function of heparanase in cancer progression

Vlodavsky Israel
Cancer and Vascular Biology Research Center, The Bruce Rappaport Faculty of Medicine, Technion, Haifa, Israel

Heparan sulfate (HS) proteoglycans play a key role in the self-assembly, insolubility and barrier properties of the extracellular matrix (ECM). Cleavage of HS therefore affects the integrity of tissues and hence normal and pathological phenomena involving cell migration and response to changes in the ECM. Mammalian heparanase, endo-•-D-glucuronidase, is synthesized as a latent 65 kDa precursor that undergoes proteolytic cleavage, yielding 8 kDa and 50 kDa subunits that heterodimerize to form a highly active enzyme. Heparanase is preferentially expressed in human tumors and its over-expression in tumor cells confers an invasive phenotype in experimental animals. Heparanase also releases angiogenic factors from the ECM and tumor microenvironment and thereby induces an angiogenic response *in vivo.* Enhanced heparanase expression correlates with metastatic potential, tumor vascularity and reduced postoperative survival of cancer patients. These observations, the anti-cancerous effect of heparanase gene silencing approaches and of heparanase-inhibiting molecules, as well as the unexpected identification of a predominant functional heparanase, suggest that the enzyme is a promising target for anti-cancer drug development. Given the potential tissue damage that could result from inadvertent cleavage of HS, tight regulation of heparanase expression and activity is essential. Of particular interest are the regulation of heparanase gene expression (i.e., promoter methylation; response to estrogen, p53) and the significance of heparanase nuclear localization, cell surface expression and secretion, HS-mediated cellular uptake of exogenous heparanase and subsequent proteolytic processing and activation of the enzyme. Heparanase also promotes cell adhesion, survival and signaling events, independent of its enzymatic activity.

0-1 Tumor Biology

Mutation analysis of the short cytoplasmic domain of the cell-cell adhesion molecule CEACAM1 identifies residues that orchestrate actin binding and lumen formation for prostate and mammary epithelial cells in a 3D model of morphogenesis

Chen CJ, Kirshner J, Sherman MA, Nguyen T, Hu W, Shively John E
City of Hope, Duarte, CA, USA

Aims: The purpose of this study was to determine the role of the cytoplasmic domain of CEACAM1 in morphogenesis.
Methods: Growth of cells in 3D culture, peptide synthesis of the cytoplasmic domain, yeast two-hybrid assay, BIAcore analysis and NMR studies.
Results: CEACAM1-4S mediates lumen formation via an apoptotic and cytoskeletal reorganization mechanism when mammary or prostate epithelial cells are grown in a 3D model of morphogenesis. Our data support the notion that CEACAM1-4S-actin binding is positively regulated by a proton switch and negatively regulated by a Ca^{2+} ion switch. We present a model of the cytoplasmic domain interaction with actin that predicts additional features that were verified by mutation analysis. We show that mutation analysis of a key threonine residue (T457D), that mimics phosphorylation at this residue, mediates apoptosis when mutant transfected cells are grown in 3D culture.
Conclusions: These studies demonstrate that a short cytoplasmic domain membrane receptor can mediate substantial intracellular signaling without the need for accessory membrane or cytoplasmic adaptor proteins.

0-2 Tumor Biology

Human monoclonal antibodies against MK-1 prepared by using human Ig gene-transferred mice

Kuroki Masahide, Yamada H, Shibaguchi H, Kinugasa T, Hachimine K, Huang J, Zhao J, Kuroki M
Dept. of Biochemistry, Fukuoka Univ. School of Medicine, Fukuoka, Japan

Aims: For efficient cancer therapy using antibodies, monoclonal antibodies (mAbs) of human origin are superior to mouse, mouse/human chimeric or humanized mAbs having minimum immunogenicity in humans and its effective collaboration with human effector immunocytes We aimed to prepare fully human mAbs against a pancarcinoma antigen, MK-1 (also known as Ep-CAM, 17-1A or GA733-2), by using human immunoglobulin (Ig) gene-transferred mouse system.
Methods: Genetically engineered mice (KM mice™), that contain the human Ig genes and in that the mouse Ig genes are knocked out, are used for immunization with recombinant MK-1. Spleen cells from the KM mice were fused with the P3-U1 mouse myeloma cells, and the resultant hybridoma clones were screened for their anti-MK-1 antibody production.
Results: Of 44 anti-MK-1 clones analyzed, two were of IgG4 and the others of IgM clones. Although the two IgG4 clones seemed to recognize the same antigenic determinant or two closely located determinants, their V regions were encoded by different light-chain genes, respectively, while their VH sequences were identical to each other. The two IgG4 and one of the IgM clones tested revealed antibody-dependent cell-mediate cytotoxicity and complement-dependent cytotoxicity, respectively, against MK-1-expressing cells *in vitro.*
Conclusions: These results suggest that these fully human mAbs generated against MK-1 and their V-region genes may be useful for antibody-based therapy of cancer.

0-3 Tumor Biology

The Ras effector RASSF2 is a novel tumor suppressor gene in human colorectal cancer

Minoru Toyota, Kimishige A, Takashi T, Yasuhisa S, Imai K
First Dept. Int. Med., Dept. Mol. Biol., Cancer Res. Inst., Sapporo Medical University, Sapporo, Japan

Aims: Activation of Ras signaling is a hallmark of colorectal cancer (CRC), but the roles of negative regulators of Ras are not fully understood. Our aim was to address that question by surveying genetic and epigenetic alterations of Ras-Ras effector genes in CRC cells.
Methods: The expression and methylation were examined using RT-PCR and bisulfite-PCR. Colony formation assays and flow cytometry were used to assess the tumor suppressor activities of RASSF1 and RASSF2. Immunofluorescence microscopy was used to determine the effect of altered RASSF2 expression on cell morphology. Mutations of K-ras, BRAF and p53 were identified using single strand conformation analysis and direct sequencing.
Results: Aberrant methylation and histone deacetylation of RASSF2 was associated with the gene's silencing in CRC. The activities of RASSF2, which were distinct from those of RASSF1, included induction of morphological changes and apoptosis; moreover, its ability to prevent cell transformation suggests RASSF2 acts as a tumor suppressor in CRC. Primary CRCs that showed K-ras/BRAF mutations also frequently showed RASSF2 methylation, and inactivation of RASSF2 enhanced K-ras-induced oncogenic transformation. RASSF2 methylation was also frequently identified in colorectal adenomas (Gastroenterol, 2005).
Conclusions: RASSF2 is a novel tumor suppressor gene that regulates Ras signaling and plays a pivotal role in the early stages of colorectal tumorigenesis.

0-4

Abstract not submitted.

0-5 Tumor Biology

Abstract not submitted.

0-6 Ovary Ca.

Peritoneal fluid cytokine evaluation for differential diagnosis of benign and malignant ovarian tumors and for disease eradication assessment.

Chechlinska Magdalena, Steffen J
Dept. of Immunology, Cancer Center and Institute of Oncology, Warsaw, Poland

Aims: To assess the potential value of local cytokine measurements for differentiating benign from malignant ovarian tumors and for evaluating the residual and/or recurrent disease in patients after treatment.
Methods: Peritoneal fluids from 53 untreated ovarian cancer patients 18 after surgery and chemotherapy,and 17 patients with benign ovarian tumors were examined for the concentrations of VEGF, bFGF, IL-6, IL-8 and M-CSF by ELISA and for CA125 -by MEIA.
Results: Malignant fluids as compared to benign ones contained significantly higher concentrations of IL-6, VEGF and CA125. However, only IL-6 and VEGF levels were found significantly higher in stage I and II ovarian cancer patients as compared to patients with benign ovarian tumors. 88% of the malignant peritoneal fluids and none of the benign ones were found to contain a combination of VEGF and IL-6 at the concentrations exceeding 400pg/ml and 300pg/ml, respectively. The levels of cytokines and CA125 measured in peritoneal fluids decreased considerably following chemotherapy and were found not to relate to the presence of residual disease nor to the disease free interval.
Conclusions: Peritoneal fluid examination for IL-6 and VEGF concentrations might be applied for differential diagnosis of ovarian tumors, but not for the evaluation of clinical outcome of ovarian cancer patients after treatment.

0-7 Ovary Ca.

Ovarian cancer vaccines

O'Brien Timothy J; Crew MD, Santin A, Cannon MJ
University of Arkansas for Medical Sciences, 4301 W. Markham, Little Rock, AR 72205 USA

The majority of ovarian cancer patients have advanced disease at the time of diagnosis, and ovarian cancer has the highest mortality rate among gynecological malignancies. Immunotherapy based on induction of tumor-specific cytotoxic T lymphocyte (CTL) responses may represent a viable treatment for these patients. The prospects for immunological treatment of cancer have risen sharply in recent years, based in part on concerted efforts to identify tumor-specific antigens that may serve as CTL targets, and in part on the application of dendritic cells (DC) as powerful inducers of tumor-specific T cell responses. We exploited the identification of a series of novel ovarian tumor antigens, including stratum corneum chymotryptic enzyme (SCCE [hK7]), for the development of therapeutic DC vaccines for ovarian cancer. These antigens are highly expressed in ovarian cancer, but not in normal ovaries or in most other normal adult tissues. Furthermore, DC pulsed with SCCE peptides can stimulate HLA A2.1-restricted $CD8^+$ CTL that kill A2.1-matched ovarian tumor cells. We have constructed peptides that encompass defined CTL epitopes and candidate $CD4^+$ helper T cell epitopes with degenerate HLA class II binding potential. DC loaded with multi-epitope peptides can then be tested for their ability to induce antigen-specific $CD8^+$ CTL responses and $CD4^+$ helper T cell responses. The rationale for this strategy is that antigen-specific $CD4^+$ T cells provide essential help for the induction of effective $CD8^+$ T cell responses, both in terms of supporting DC maturation and also for supporting the persistence of antigen-specific $CD8^+$ T cells in vivo. Peptide-loaded DC immunotherapy that is capable of inducing both $CD8^+$ CTL responses and $CD4^+$ helper T cell responses thus offers greater potential for inducing durable immune responses and clinical benefit than treatment with DC loaded with $CD8^+$ CTL peptide epitopes alone.

0-8 Ovary Ca.

Hereditary-Breast Ovarian Cancer (HBOC) syndrome: History, tumor complement and management

Lynch Henry T, Casey MJ, Snyder C, Lynch JF
Creighton University School of Medicine, Omaha, Nebraska

Aims: To trace the history of hereditary breast and ovarian cancers. The potential effectiveness of prophylactic breast and gynecologic surgery will be discussed.
Methods: Studies of extended cancer family pedigrees and our review of medical records and pathology have enabled us to develop cancer prevention models for women of hereditary breast ovarian cancer (HBOC) syndrome kindreds. The clinical and pathological characteristics of the HBOC syndrome, which now is recognized to include peritoneal serous carcinoma, fallopian tube carcinoma and possibly endometrial papillary serous carcinoma, together with advances in molecular genetics, permit the diagnosis of this disease with a high degree of accuracy.Definition of the cardinal clinical features and pathology of HBOC syndrome have been essential for design and recommendation of management strategies.
Results: With surgical prophylaxis, more than 90% of breast cancers and approximately 95% of ovarian cancers can be prevented in female carriers of *BRCA1* and *BRCA2* mutations.Prophylactic oophorectomy, alone, has been associated with ~ 50% reduction of breast cancer in women with genetic susceptibilities.
Conclusions: Largely through the early identification of women at risk from HBOC syndrome families, coupled with the option of appropriate prophylactic surgery, where we employ complete salpingoophorectomy with hysterectomy, cancer morbidity and mortality have been significantly reduced in *BRCA1* and *BRCA2* mutation carriers.

0-9 Ovary Ca.

Pattern of release of oncological biomarkers in benign and malignant diseases of the ovary

Stieber Petra, Kümper C[1], Holdenrieder S, Hofmann K, Burges A[1]
Institute of Clinical Chemistry, Department of Gynecology[1], University of Munich, Munich, Germany

Aims: Due to the lack of organ specificity of most biomarkers and the lack of tumor specificity of all biomarkers serological diagnostic oncology actually mainly focuses on follow up care of tumor diseases using a single marker with the best profile of specificity and sensitivity for this purpose. More and more it becomes evident that malignant diseases lead to a significant release or non release of multiple biomarkers and that the sum of these informations leads to an increase of diagnostic, differential diagnostic or prognostic capacities.
Methods: We investigated the sera of 120 patients suffering from ovarian cancer at time of diagnosis before first treatment and of 442 patients with various benign gynaecological disorders using the following parameters: CEA, AFP, CYFRA 21-1, NSE, CA 19-9, CA 15-3, CA 72-4, CA 125, S100, PSA, fPSA, ßHCG (Elecsys, Roche).
Results: in benign gynecological diseases some biomarkers showed no increased release as compared to the frequency distribution in healthy individuals (AFP, S100, PSA, NSE), some showed slightly increased release (CYFRA 21-1, CEA, CA 15-3), some significant increase (CA 125, CA 72.4, CA 19-9, ßHCG). In ovarian cancer patients the highest release could be observed for CA 125 (median 286 U/ml, 95th percentile:3357 U/ml) and CYFRA 21-1 (median 3 ng/ml, 95th percentile 69 ng/ml), followed by CA 15-3, CA 72-4 and CA 19-9, resulting in a sensitivity of 65% for CA 125 and CYFRA 21-1 each at a specificity of 95%. At a specificity of 100% CYFRA 21-1 is clearly superior to CA 125 (39% sensitivity versus 24%), the combined determination of both markers yielded by far the best results and increases the true positive findings up to 49%.
Conclusions: the combined analysis of the frequency and the extent of release and non-release of oncological biomarkers reveals a high potential for diagnosis and differential diagnosis.

0-10 Ovary Ca.

The predictive value of CA 125 and TPS levels after 3 chemotherapy courses in ovarian cancer patients.

Van Dalen Arie, Favier J[1], Hallesleben E[1], Burges A[2], Stieber P[2], de Bruijn HWA[3], Fink D[4], Giai M[5], McGing P[6], Harlozinska A[7], Kainz Ch[8], Markowska J[9], Molina R[10], Sturgeon C[11], Bowman A[12], Einarsson R[13], Goike H[14].

Institute of Tumour Marker Oncology, Gouda, The Netherlands, [1]Groene Hart Ziekenhuis, Gouda, The Netherlands, [2]Klinikum Grosshadern, Munich, Germany, [3]Lab of Obst & Gyn, University Hospital, Groningen. The Netherlands, [4]Dept of Obst & Gyn, University Hospital, Zurich, Switzerland, [5]Clinica Pinna Pintor, Torino, Italy, [6]Dept of Biochemistry, Mater Misericordiae, Dublin, Ireland, [7]Dept of Tumor Immunology, University of Medicine, Wroclaw, Poland, [8]Dept of Gyn & Obst, Vienna University Medical School, Vienna, Austria, [9]Dept of Oncology, Medical School, Poznan, Poland, [10]Lab of Clinical Chem, Hospital Clinico Provincial, Barcelona, Spain, [11]Clinical Biochem, Royal Infirmary, Edinburgh, United Kingdom, [12]Dept of Oncology, Western General Hospital, Edinburgh, United Kingdom, [13]CanAg Diagnostics AB, Gothenburg, Sweden, [14]IDL Biotech, Stockholm, Sweden

Aims: A multicentre evaluation of the predictive value of CA125 & TPS.
Methods: 10-year overall survival depending on TM levels (N=213).
Results: It is confirmed that the TPS levels after 3 chemotherapy courses is an independent variable of 10-year overall survival. In patients with a CA 125 level<25 kU/l after 3 chemotherapy courses (OS=28%), 11 patients showed a TPS level>100 U/l. 8 out of these patients (73%) died within 2 years and 10 patients (91%) died within 10 years.
Conclusions: Our publication in Gyn Oncol 79, 444-450 (2000) about the predictive value of CA 125 and TPS levels in 2-year OS is confirmed.

0-11 Ovary Ca.

Prognostic kallikrein markers for ovary cancer

Barak Vivian, Sherman Y, Edelman D, Peretz T, Diamandis EP
Immunology Lab for Tumor Diagnosis, Oncology Dep., Pathology Dep. Hadassah University Hospital, Jerusalem, Israel and Pathology Laboratory Medicine Dep., Mount Sinai Hospital, Toronto, ON.

Aims: To examine the immunostaining of KLK6 and KLK10 in ovarian neoplasms and evaluate correlations between intensity and the histological subtyping and grading of tumors, defining potential uses of the differential expression as morphologic prognostic markers in these tumors.
Methods: We have analyzed specimens from 25 normal ovarian tissues, 30 ovarian tissues with benign epithelial neoplasms, 19 with various mesenchymal tumors and 40 - carcinomas of various histological sub-types. We employed KLK6 and KLK10-specific polyclonal rabbit antibody and avidin-biotin to localize KLK6 and KLK10 respectively, by immunohistochemistry (IHC).
Results: Both kallikreins were markedly expressed in the cytoplasm of carcinoma cells of various histological types and grades .KLK6 and KLK10 were not stained in normal cells, stromal cells, tumor cells of mesenchymal origin, and only negligibly expressed in cells of the epithelial component of benign ovarian neoplasms. The staining intensity in the positive carcinoma cells was found to differentiate well between the main 2 histological sub types, so that the serous papillary ca, showed a higher staining intensity than the mucinous ca. Comparison of the staining characteristics in the various sub-groups (as defined by histological grading), revealed a tendency towards increasing intensity of expression the higher the tumor grade, being accentuated in foci of anaplastic carcinoma.Tissue expression of KLK 6 and 10 was compared to serum levels of CA 125 and clinical parameters. as well as to KLK6 and KLK 10 serum levels.
Conclusions: IHC expression of both KLK6 and KLK10 in ovarian cancers follows the path of classical morphological criteria for tumor aggressiveness, and may prove to be a useful diagnostic tool for more accurately defining the future biological behaviour and therapeutic response of these tumors.

0-12 Endometrium Cancer

Computer assisted tissue image analysis in endometrium cancer

Vasilios Tanos, Neophytou M, Pattichis C
Computer Science Department, University of Cyprus, Cyprus

Aims: The objective of this study was to develop a complete system for image analysis during hysteroscopy, in order to increase intaoperative diagnosis and its accuracy.
Methods: 500 hysteroscopy images from 37 patients, with suspicious endometrial pathology were used. A standardized protocol for capturing and analysis, color correction and histograms, multiscale analysis, texture feature algorithms, statistical tests (Wilcox Rank Sum Test) and neural networks were applied for the identification of endometrial hyperplasia and cancer.
Results: Results showed that suspicious areas can be identified from normal ROIs (Regions of Interest) using the CATIA (**C**omputer **A**ssisted **T**issue **I**mage **A**nalysis) system. Statistical tests of the texture features, such as entropy, homogeneity and variance, have significant difference between normal and abnormal ROIs and can be used for the classification of different lesions. Training neural networks can classify different ROIs according to the histopathological examination. In the hyperplasia case the percentage of correct classifications was 90% in normal ROIs and 82% in abnormal ROIs respectively.
Conclusions: The need of using CATIA during hysteroscopy can increase diagnosis accuracy. Using clinical data and tumour markers the sensitivity of this method can be increased.

0-13 Standardization

Interference by heterophilic antibodies in a T84.66 based CEA assay. Fab-, and $F(ab')_2$ -fragments compared to recombinant scFv as solid phase reagents.

Nustad Kjell, Bjerner J, Børmer O, Paus E, Varaas T, Olsen K, and Warren D
Central Laboratory, Rikshospitalet-Radiumhospitalet HF, Montebello, 0310 Oslo, Norway.

Aims: We have shown that in vivo biotinylated single-chain (scFv) used as capture reagent decrease the incident of interference from heterophilic antibodies (Warren et al., Clin. Chem. 51, 830-838, 2005). Now we want to test the hypothesis that Fab-fragments with biotinylation in free SH-group could represent a better reagent than $F(ab')_2$-fragments with random biotinylation in NH-groups used in present assays.
Methods: Patients sera were selected from 11 000 patient screened for interference. The assays using scFv and $F(ab')_2$ as solid phase reagents are described (Warren et al. 2005). $F(ab')_2$-fragments was prepared by clevage of IgG using bromelain. Fab-fragment was prepared by reduction of $F(ab')_2$ with 2-mercaptoethylamin followed by gel filtration, and biotinylation with maleimidopropionyl biocytin.
Results: Assay kinetics and standard curves were similar with all binding proteins used in excess in immunometric assays. The scFv-assay used a buffer containing bovine IgG and aggregated mouse IgG1 as blocking agents, whereas the Fab- and $F(ab')_2$ –fragment assays used buffer containing only BSA.
Conclusions: Heterophilic antibodies affected the assays in the following order: IgG >> $F(ab')_2$ > Fab' > scFv. However, even the best assay needed aggregated MAK33 to avoid interference in some serum samples.

0-14 Standardization

Standardization of tumour marker measurements: Progress and problems

Sturgeon Catharine
Department of Clinical Biochemistry, Royal Infirmary of Edinburgh, Edinburgh, UK

Long-term monitoring of cancer patients with tumor markers presents major analytical challenges, since patients may change hospital and laboratories may change tumour marker methods during the relevant time period. While ideally results obtained in different methods would be fully interchangeable, data from External Quality Assessment Schemes confirm that this is not the case, with between method coefficients of variation in excess of 20% still observed for some tumour markers.

How best to improve the standardization and comparability of results obtained using different methods has therefore been the subject of much debate, but it is generally agreed that this requires

- Clear nomenclature.
- Accurate calibration with well-characterized International Standards.
- Improved understanding of what different methods measure.
- Broad agreement about the clinically most appropriate antibody combinations.
- Improved understanding of method vulnerability to clinically relevant interferences.

Considerable progress has already been made for some tumour markers (e.g. PSA, hCG), but the situation is much less satisfactory for others (e.g. CA125). By assessing the current status of standardization of major tumour markers, priorities for future improvement can be identified.

0-15 Proteomics

Cancer biomarker discovery and validation by mass spectrometry

Diamandis Eleftherios P
Clinical Biochemistry, Mount Sinai Hospital, University Health Network and Toronto Medical Laboratories and Department of Laboratory Medicine and Pathobiology, University of Toronto

Aims: The past decade has seen an explosion of published data on the applications of mass spectrometry in cancer research, but despite the wealth of literature, findings vary. Mass spectrometry's shortcomings need to be emphasized to avoid premature implementation into clinical practice.
Methods: Current literature reveals that mass spectrometry has been applied in two different settings in cancer research, namely as a biomarker discovery and as a cancer diagnostic tool. This method identified only a handful of putative new cancer biomarkers, most of which are acute phase proteins.
Results: Mass spectrometry has been used to diagnose a variety of cancers: ovarian, breast, prostate, bladder, pancreatic, head and neck, lung, colon, melanoma and hepatocellular carcinoma, with diagnostic sensitivities and specificities varying from 75-100%. Some of the identified limitations of this approach include: a) the distinguishing peaks between cancer and non-cancer patients are different between the various research groups, b) the identity of the distinguishing molecules is unknown in most cases, or signify acute phase reactants and/or high abundance molecules, likely representing cancer epiphenomena. Despite the wealth of literature, no independent and blinded validation studies have been conducted as yet.
Conclusions: I conclude that despite the reported high sensitivity and specificity of mass spectrometry for cancer diagnosis, the lack of validation and standardization through large, multicentered clinical trials, precludes its implementation in clinical practice at present.

0-16 Proteomics

The impact of protein profiling using antibody arrays in cancer research

Sanchez-Carbayo Marta
Memorial Sloan-Kettering Cancer Center, NY, USA

The advent of high-throughput proteomic technologies is complementing the information gained through gene expression profiling analyses. Antibody arrays enable detection of multiple proteins simultaneously. The methods and applications of antibody arrays are increasing in scope and effectiveness for cancer diagnostics and characterization of the biology underlining tumor progression. The main advantage of the technology over other proteomic approaches resides on that the identities of the measured proteins are known or can be readily characterized. The requirement of low sample volumes of both precious clinical material and antibodies, together with their format versatility and high reproducibility support their impact and variety of clinical applications in cancer research. The multiplexed measurements of proteins allow screening of disease biomarkers that are potentially valuable for diagnosis, outcome prognosis or surrogate predictors of drug response. The standard concept of individual cancer biomarker will eventually be modified by clusters or groups of proteins that better reveal associations between cancer subtypes and clinical outcomes. Moreover, antibody arrays enable exploring posttranslational changes or differential expression levels of proteins, and test the involvement of signaling pathways on tumorigenesis and cancer progression. Thus, antibody arrays techniques are likely to markedly accelerate the rate of biomarker discovery and characterization of cancer-specific pathways that will lead eventually to the development of individualized therapies that take into account markers of disease predisposition and therapeutic response.

0-17 Proteomics

Interrelationships between – omics and imaging in cancer disease

Oehr Peter
University Bonn, Germany

Aims: There is an increasing number of assays and technologies emerging within genomics, proteomics and metabolomics, which can be also summarized as "-omics". These techniques can be used for in-vitro determination of risk, state and follow-up of disease at hand of new biomarkers. The purpose is to introduce to what can be achieved to date based on "-omics", in connection to new imaging technologies, to bring forward novel strategies for the non-invasive and clinically relevant tumor diagnosis, -location and –therapy control.
Methods: Examples are given for -omics biomarker profiling and the resulting systems which can be applied in imaging.
Results: Imaging based on "-omics" has become an important tool in biology and medicine for non-invasive detecting and monitoring metabolic changes in-vivo. Advances have been made including tissue recognition by microscopy, radionuclide imaging, such as positron emission tomography (PET) and single photon emission tomography (SPECT), magnetic resonance (MR) imaging and spectroscopy, bioluminescence imaging and various fluorescence imaging techniques, such as fluorescence-mediated tomography (FMT) and near-infrared fluorescence (NIRF) reflectance imaging.
Conclusions: Connecting the relationships between genomic-, proteomic- and metabolomic changes, and application of this knowledge to non-invasive in-vivo imaging is paving the avenue to "ontime" understanding of oncodevelopmental biology and medicine.

0-18 Proteomics

Biomarkers for ovarian cancer and the host response amplification cascade

Fung Eric T
Ciphergen Biosystems, Fremont, CA, USA

Aims: Protein expression profiling has been increasingly used to discover and characterize biomarkers that can be used for diagnostic, prognostic or therapeutic purposes. Most proteomic studies published to date have identified relatively abundant host response proteins as candidate biomarkers, which are often dismissed because of an apparent lack of specificity.
Methods: SELDI-TOF-MS assays were constructed and applied to serum samples taken from individuals with different cancers and healthy controls. Multivariate analysis was performed on the resulting peaks.
Results: We demonstrate that 2 host response proteins previously identified as candidate markers for early stage ovarian cancer, transthyretin and inter-alpha trypsin inhibitor heavy chain 4 (ITIH4), are posttranslationally modified. Quantitative measurements of these modifications using chromatographic and antibody-based ProteinChip array assays reveal that these posttranslational modifications occur to different extents in different cancers and that multivariate analysis permits the derivation of algorithms to improve the classification of these cancers.
Conclusions: Assays using Surface Enhanced Laser Desorption/Ionization Time of Flight Mass Spectrometry (SELDI-TOF-MS) may provide a means to confer specificity to these proteins because of their ability to detect and quantitate multiple posttranslationally modified forms of these proteins in a single assay. We have termed this process host response protein amplification cascade (HRPAC), since the process of synthesis, posttranslational modification and metabolism of host response proteins amplifies the signal of potentially low-abundant biologically active disease markers such as enzymes.

0-19 Proteomics

High throughput profiling of cancer serum biomarkers

Pawlak D, Zarozinski C, Frisse Andrea, Parker B
Schleicher & Schuell BioScience

Profiling biomarkers in complex mixtures such as serum is challenging since the dynamic range of proteins in the serum proteome is broad. Schleicher & Schuell BioScience has developed a single capture antibody chip that enables clinical researchers to simultaneously screen hundreds of circulating cancer serum biomarkers from two serum samples. Single capture antibody chips combined with a protein labeling and fluorescent detection system offers a new proteomics capability to measure known serum biomarkers that does not require mass spectrometry instrumentation. Direct labeling of serum proteins with small molecular haptens was performed using chemistries that target multiple amino acids. The abundance of a 120 classical cancer biomarkers, cytokines, and chemokines were measured directly from eight microliters of serum. Biomarker profiling data demonstrate pattern reproducibility from serum obtained from bladder, breast, colon and prostate cancer patients compared to age- and gender-matched control serum samples.

0-20 Hematology

Hemangioblasts in chronic myeloid leukemia (CML) and its neovasculogenesis

Prindull Gregor
Dept. Pediatrics, University of Göttingen, Germany

Hemangioblasts are the earliest common endothelial/hematopoietic stem cells identifiable during ontogeny. We propose, as a working hypothesis, to consider the bi-directional, reversible potential of hematopoietic-endothelial gene transcription as complementary parts of a functional entity comprising hemangioblasts, endothelial progenitors, and hematopoietic stem cells in terms of ontogeny, angiogenesis, post-natal development and, perhaps, leukemogenesis. This extends the concept of hematopoietic stem cell plasticity (Quesenberry 2002) to include endotheliopoiesis. The existence of hemangioblasts in adults can be interpreted in at least 2 ways: 1) as a remnant minority population of a hemato/endothelial stem cell reservoir surviving from ontogeny, and/or 2) as plastic re-activation by reversal of embryonal pathways through de-differentiation of repressed receptors. Size and availability of hemato/endothelial reservoirs in individual patients has clinical significance, e.g. in aplastic anemias and leukemias/angiogenesis.

The identification of BCR/ABL tyrosine kinase fusion proteins in endothelial Flk1+ CML cells characterizes them as part of the leukemic clone. This extends the concept of a functional hemato/endothelial entity to leukemogenesis and suggests that hemangioblasts, rather than commited hematopoietic stem cells, are the true target cells for the initiating oncogenic event in CML. The oncogenic time window for CML could be as early as the embryonal hemangioblast, i.e. during one of the first steps of embryonal stem cell differentiation. It is not known what the relations are of the other leukemias to hemangioblasts.

0-21 Hematology

Leukemia: Stem cells, maturation arrest and differentiation therapy.

Sell S
Ordway Research Institute,Wadsworth Center, Empire State Plaza, NYSDOH, Albany, NY, USA

Aims: To expand the hypothesis of maturation arrest of cancer to human myeloid leukemias and show how effective therapy results in removal of the maturation block and allows leukemic cells to terminally differentiate.
Methods: The genetic lesions of human leukemias are related to the stage of differentiation for representative leukemias. Then the effect of specific molecular targeted therapies directed to the genetic lesions is described for three models of acute and chronic myeloid leukemias.
Results: In chronic myeloid leukaemia the bcr-able translocation produces a fusion protein that acts as a tyrosine kinase and causes constitutive activation at the myelocyte level. This activation may be inhibited by imatinib mesylate (Gleevec, STI-571) which allows the myelocytes to terminally differentiate. In acute promyelocytic leukaemia the fusion product of the *PML-RAR* produces activation at the promyelocyte level. This may be inactivated by treatment with retinoids, which bind to the fusion protein and cause it to be destroyed. In one common type of acute leukaemia, with arrest at the myeloid precursor level, there is a mutation in tyrosine kinase 3 (FLT3), a transmembrane tyrosine kinase which acts though Src family tyrosine kinases. This may be blocked by agents that inhibit farnesyl transferase (tipifarnib ® or Ionafarnig). In each of these examples specific inhibition of the altered activation molecules allow the cells to differentiate and die.
Conclusions: Human myeloid leukemias provide models of the principle of maturation arrest of cancer.When the specific molecular lession is known, treatment may be directed at the activation signal. Blocking of the signal allows the cells to overcome the stage at which they are arrested and terminally differentiate.

0-22 Hematology

Diagnosis, differential diagnosis and monitoring of monoclonal gammopathies

Lamerz Rolf[1], Wick M[2], Eichhorn P[2], Holdenrieder S[2]
[1]Medical Department II, [2]Institute of Clinical Chemistry, LMU-Klinikum-Grosshadern, University of Munich, Germany

Monoclonal gammopathy is expressed by a plasma cell dyscrasia detected initially often incidentally or later by clinical symptoms (fatigue, bone pain, infections, renal insufficiency). Initial laboratory investigations comprise electrophoretic detection of an M-gradient (spike) in serum and/or urine followed by immunoglobulin class and type characterization by means of immunofixation electrophoresis and quantitation of the paraprotein and uninvolved immunoglobulins by use of densitometry or nephelometry. Alterations in the extended laboratory, bone marrow, squelettal status and other interdisciplinary investigations allow for ascertaining the dignity of the detected protein for a clear diagnosis and indication of further monitoring without (MGUS, SMM) or with necessary treatment (MM, MW). Multiple myeloma (MM, a WHO classified B cell lymphoma) is characterized predominantly by more osteolytic than osteoporotic bone alterations and Morbus Waldenstroem (MW, lymphoplasmocytoid lymphoma) more by lymph node, spleen and liver increases and blood circulatory and bleeding complications supported by the large IgM molecule size and both entities in follow-up by renal insufficiency, immunodeficiency and more seldom by AL amyloidosis. Ascertaining of diagnosis and treatment indication as well as treatment monitoring are of outmost importance and obviously effected by clinical-chemical, histologic and imaging investigations.

0-23 Hematology

Immunophenotyping – diagnosis and prognosis of hematological malignancies

Fibach Eitan
Dept. of Hematology, Hadassah University Hospital, Jerusalem, Israel

Aims: Flow cytometry immunophenotyping has become a routine methodology in conjunction with morphology, cytochemistry, molecular and chromosomal analyses for characterization of malignant cells of the lympho-hematopoietic system. In addition to assisting in diagnosis, the procedure provides a measure of the efficacy of the treatment, the expression of cellular antigens available for immunotherapy, it often reveals the presence of Minimal Residual Disease, and in some cases, the results have a prognosis value. Other cellular properties that can be studied include evaluation of the Multi-Drug Resistance phenotype with anti-P-glycoprotein antibodies or by a functional assay using rhodamine-123, the cell cycle and ploidy status, oxidative stress and the expression of various oncogenes and anti-tumor proteins.
Methods: Single-cell suspensions are stained with a combination of fluorochrome-conjugated antibodies or other fluorescence agents. Flow cytometry allows simultaneous measurement of cell size, granularity as well as four (or more) different fluorochromes.
Results: The acute leukemia panel is designed primarily to quantify leukemic blasts and determine their cellular origin - myeloid or lymphoid, and sub-classification. For lymphomas/lymphoproliferative disorders phenotyping includes their characterization as B or T cells. For B cell malignancies, the presence of a monoclonal population expressing restricted •immunoglobulin light chains, and for T cell malignancies, the existence of an abnormal T cell phenotype.
Conclusions: Flow cytometry allows multi-parameter analysis of different subpopulations of peripheral blood, bone marrow and lymph nodes cells.

0-24 Hematology

Inhibition of B16 melanoma metastases by therapy with M20 IL-1 inhibitor (a new cytokine)

[1]Barak V[1], Yanai P[1], Halperin T[1], Vlodavsky I[2], Slavin S[3], Weiss Lola[3]
[1]Immunology Lab for Tumor Diagnosis, [2]Oncology Dept, [3]Bone Marrow Transplant Unit, Hadassah University Hospital, Jerusalem, Israel

Aims: To examine the effect of the M20 IL-1 Inhibitor (a new cytokine) on lung metastases formation in an *in vivo* model of B16 Melanoma
Methods: We previously established in in vivo models that M20 IL-1 Inhibitor is a potent anti-inflammatory agent reducing fever,leukocytosis, local inflammation, IL-1 induced changes in fibrinogen, corticosterone and cations serum levels. Most importantly, M20 IL-1 Inhibitor prevented the onset of Rheumatoid Arthritis (RA) and reduced its severity in a rat model and was also effective in reducing various parameters of an autoimmune disease (SLE). We used an *in vivo* B16 melanoma model for developing lung metastases and evaluated their size, number, lungs' weight, and also the proliferation of melanoma cells *in vitro* in the presence of this inhibitor.
Results: Our results showed a significant reduction in the number of melanoma lung metastases (45-55%) in mice treated with M20 IL-1 Inhibitor (50 or 100 U/mouse). There was also a significant reduction in the size of the melanoma metastases (~60%) and in the weight of the treated lungs. These results are similar to *in vitro* findings showing a reduction of growth and number of melanoma cells *in vitro* or in mice's blood, after treatment with this inhibitor .Pathological sections of the lungs show the effect and correlate to the findings.
Conclusions: We conclude that the M20 IL-1 Inhibitor is active in the inhibition of B16 Melanoma lung metastases, implying a role of this molecule, as a new therapeutic and immunotherapy modality in melanoma.

0-25 S-100 Workshop

TD-11 Workshop report: Characterization of monoclonal antibodies to S-100 proteins

Paus Elisabeth[1], H.Olsen K[1], Haugen Mads H. [2], Flatmark K.[2], Maelandsmo G. M.[2]
[1]Central Laboratory and [2]Department of Tumor Biology, The Norwegian Radium Hospital, Oslo, Norway

Aim: To investigate the specificity and characteristics of monoclonal antibodies submitted to the ISOBM TD-11 S100 Workshop
Methods: Fourteen antibodies directed against various S100 proteins were submitted to the ISOBM TD-11 Workshop from collaborating laboratories. Reference antigens comprising S100 and S100BB from human brain, recombinant human S100B, recombinant human S100 A4, and bovine S100A1A1, S100A1B, S100BB, as well as polyclonal rabbit anti S100BB were also obtained. Binding studies were done using either ^{125}I-labelled antigens or ^{125}I-labelled antibodies. Sandwich immunoassays were performed with all pair combinations of antibodies and all the available antigens, as well as cross-inhibition of antibody binding to S100BB, and Western blotting analysis.
Results: Eight of the fourteen monoclonal antibodies recognized both human and bovine S100BB. One antibody recognized only recombinant monomer S100B, one was specific for S100A1A1, three antibodies reacted only with recombinant S100A4, while one antibody did not show any reactivity towards the available antigens. It was possible to classify the B-specific antibodies into four groups from the cross-inhibition and immunoassay studies. Western blot analysis under reducing conditions partly agreed with the classification of specificities towards the different S-100 antigens.

0-26 S-100 Workshop

Abstract not submitted.

0-27 Gastrointestinal Ca.

Abnormal expression of M1/MUC5AC mucin during colon carcinogenesis.

Bara Jacques
U-673 INSERM, Hôpital St-Antoine, 75012 Paris, France

Aims: To study the possible use of the M1/MUC5AC mucin as an early marker of human colon carcinogenesis.
Methods: M1/MUC5AC mucin was characterised using 8 monoclonal antibodies against M1 epitopes located in the small globular regions of the tandem repeat domain as well as in the C- and N- terminal globular regions of the MUC5AC apomucin. The expression of this mucin was studied by immunoperoxidase methods on tissue samples and IRMA on mucus samples. After surgery, colon tissues were obtained and colon mucus was scraped from fresh tissues of patients with adenocarcinomas (n=56), diverticulitis (n=25, control group), normal colon (n = 4), ulcerative colitis (n=12) and Crohn disease (n=10).
Results: The M1/MUC5AC mucin, absent from the normal colon, is abnormally expressed in adenomas, hyperplastic polyps, and the macroscopically normal mucosa adjacent to adenocarcinoma. In addition, we detected this mucin in the aberrant crypt foci, regarded as precursors of precancerous lesions as defined in rat colon carcinogenesis. Immunoradiometric assays showed that this mucin is more expressed in cancer patients than in the control group (specificity = 0,69; sensitivity = 0,84). In addition, the M1/MUC5AC mucin is strongly expressed in 100% of patients with ulcerative colitis and somewhat less in patients with Crohn disease.
Conclusions: The M1/MUC5AC mucin, expressed in the precancerous lesions as well as in inflammatory bowel diseases, suggests a probable link between both these pathologies. Therefore, this marker could be a useful tool for the detection and survey of the precancerous lesions in the colon.

0-28 Gastrointestinal Ca.

Immunopathology of chronic intestinal inflammation

Hammarström Marie-Louise, Fahlgren A, Forsberg G, Hernell O, Danielsson Å, Hammarström S
Depts. of Immunology, Paediatrics, and Gastroenterology, Umeå University, Umeå, Sweden

Aims: To investigate the role of intestinal epithelial cells (iECs) in innate immune responses in inflammation by analysis of anti-microbial peptides, mucins and glycocalyx components.
Methods: Expression of alpha-defensins HD5 and HD6, beta-defensins HBD1 through 4, MUC2 and MUC3, and CEA family members CEA, CEACAM1, CEACAM6 and CEACAM7 was analyzed in iECs of patients with celiac disease (CD), Crohn's disease (MbC) and ulcerative colitis (UC) and controls by real-time quantitative RT-PCR and immunohistochemistry. Intestinal cell lines exposed to bacteria or treated with cytokines were also studied.
Results: HD5 and HD6 were normally expressed in small but not large intestine. Inflammation caused HD-5 and HD6 production in colon and increased production in small intestine of CD but not MbC patients. CD patients also showed an increased production of MUC2. HBD1 was constitutively expressed and expression levels were not changed by inflammation. Production of HBD2 to 4 was induced by inflammation in colon but not in small intestine. Expression of glycocalyx components (CEACAMs and MUC3) was generally not affected by inflammation. The expression level of HBD2 in cell lines was increased by exposure to bacteria while HBD3, HBD4 and CEACAMs were increased by proinflammatory cytokines.
Conclusions: The innate immune response at the intestinal epithelial surface is increased in inflammation. Activation seems to occur both directly by bacteria and indirectly by cytokines from local immune cells.

0-29 Gastrointestinal Ca.

Biomarker selection for detection of occult tumour cells in lymph nodes of colorectal cancer patients using real-time quantitative RT-PCR

Hammarström M-L[1], Ohlsson L[1], Israelsson A[1], Öberg Å[2], Lindmark G[3], Hammarström Sten[1]
Departments of Immunology[1] and Surgery[2], Umeå University, Umeå
[3]Surgery, Helsingborgs Lasaret, Helsingborg, Sweden

Aims: To determine which properties of a biomarker are important for identification of disseminated CRC cells in lymph nodes.
Methods: A test-set of 129 lymph nodes from 51 CRC patients (Dukes' A - D) and 10 controls as well as primary tumours, normal colon epithelium and immune cells was analyzed at the mRNA level using quantitative real-time RT-PCR assays for the following biomarkers: CEA, CEACAM1-S/-L, CEACAM6, CEACAM7-1/-2, MUC2, MMP7, and CK20. The biomarkers were ranked according to: 1) detection of H&E positive nodes, 2) detection of Dukes' A and B patients, who during the follow-up period had developed metastases and 3) detection of Dukes' C and D patients using the highest value of control nodes as cut-off.
Results: The biomarkers fell into three groups: CEA, MUC2 and CK20 had high discriminating power; CEACAM6, CEACAM7-2 and CEACAM1-S had some discriminating power while CEACAM1-L, CEACAM7-1 and MMP7 were not discriminatory. CEA was slightly better than MUC2 and CK20, positively identifying all individuals defined by the three criteria except two Dukes' D patients.
Conclusions: CEA mRNA was superior due to very high expression in columnar epithelial cells and goblet cells, no down-regulation in tumour cells and no expression in immune cells.

0-30 Gastrointestinal Ca.

Nucleosomes predict early the response to radiochemotherapy in patients with colorectal and pancreatic cancer

Kremer Andreas[1], Holdenrieder S[1], Stieber P[1], Wilkowski R[2], Nagel D[1], Seidel D[1]
[1]Institute of Clinical Chemistry, [2]Institute of Radiotherapy and Radiooncology,
University Hospital Munich-Grosshadern, Munich, Germany

Background: As radiochemotherapy is very toxic and macroscopic effects are often seen late, biochemical markers for the early prediction of therapy response are needed.
Patients and methods: Courses of nucleosomes, CEA, CA 19-9 and CYFRA 21-1 were analyzed in sera of 29 patients with colorectal cancer and 32 patients with pancreatic cancer during radiochemotherapy and were correlated with therapy efficacy.
Results: During the first week of therapy, nucleosome levels increased rapidly followed by a slow decrease. Other oncological biomarkers only showed slight variations. In colorectal cancer patients receiving postoperative therapy (N=7) nucleosomes, CEA and CYFRA 21-1 levels were generally lower than in patients with preoperative (N=13; p=0.008; p=0.062; p=0.041) or relapse therapy (N=9; p=0.014; p=0.027; p=0.051), however not CA 19-9 (p=0.497; p=0.203). In the subgroup of preoperatively treated patients, those with good response to therapy had a significantly smaller area under the curve of days 1-3 of nucleosomes (AUC 1-3) than those with progressive disease (p=0.028). In contrast, CEA, CA 19-9 and CYFRA 21-1 showed no correlation with therapy efficacy. In pancreatic cancer patients, the AUC 1-3 of nucleosomes correlated significantly with the progression-free interval (p=0.008).
Conclusion: The changes in nucleosome levels already during the initial treatment phase indicate the efficacy of radiochemotherapy in patients with colorectal and pancreatic cancer.

0-31 Gastrointestinal Ca.

Presence of DNA sequences, identical to hepatitis C virus, in the DNA of patients' hepatocytes and mononuclear cells.

Zemer R[1], Adler S[1], Cohen YK[2], Naftaly T[2], Schilman Y[1], Klein Ami[1]
[1]Molecular Biology Laboratory, [2] Gastrointestinal Unit, Meir Hospital, Kfar Saba and Sackler School of Medicine, Tel Aviv University, Israel

Aims: Evidence shows that essential mixed cryoglobulinemia (EMC), B-cell-non-Hodgkin-lymphoma (NHL) and hepatoma are associated with Hepatitis C Virus (HCV) infections . HCV is an RNA virus which differs from retroviruses and possesses no integration potential. However, because of its oncogenic potential, we tried to detect its presence in the genome of mononuclear cells (MNC) of either HCV (+) patients with EMC (n=10) or NHL (n=3) and in hepatocytes of HCV (+) patients (n=16).
Methods: DNA was isolated from mononuclear cells or heptocytes of the HCV (+) patients and controls (n=22). Preliminary screening studies for detection of integration were carried out by PCR and seminested PCR processes. Positive results were further investigated by means of Southern analysis of patient's DNA. as well as probe hybridization and sequencing of PCR products of patient's DNA. .
Results: One of the EMC group and one of the HCV(+) hepatitis were found positive demonstrating presence of HCV sequences in their genome.
Conclusions: HCV is a virus without a known DNA intermediate stage of replication. As much as we are aware this is the first demonstration of the possible integration of HCV sequences into the DNA of MNC and hepatocytes of HCV (+) patients.

0-32 Gastrointestinal Ca.

CA 19-9 in pancreatic cancer – from diagnosis to therapy

Klapdor Rainer
ZeTDT GmbH, Internal Medicine, Hamburg, Germany

Inspite of a lot of work to improve sensitivity and specificity as well as assay procedures and quality control CA 19-9 failed to fullfill the criteria of an ideal TM. Nevertheless, it`s rather high sensitivity for non-resectable/ metastatic PaCa stages and for earlier detection of tumor recurrence after surgery compared to imaging methods offers CA 19-9 as a valid TM for follow-up after primary diagnosis and for monitoring palliative treatment modalities. CA 19-9 proved to be a more sensitive parameter to therapeutic activities compared to clinical signs, other laboratory data and modern imaging methods. Monthly serum CA 19-9 determinations combined with bi-monthly imaging procedures allow detection of antitumoral efficacy of cytostatics as well as of new tumor progress after PFST in general within 6-8 weeks. Combination of CA19-9 + imaging methods is therefore offering the concept of an efficacy orientated sequential poly- (EOSPC) or multimodal therapy (EOSMT) also for tumors with short survival times like PaCa . Clinical experience during the past 7 years underlines the concept of EOSPC: median survival 4-6 mo without effective treatment, 10-12 mo with 1 effective and more than 20 mo in patients with more than 1 effective treatment (M0 as well as M1 tumors). Furthermore, the involvement of CA 19-9 in the follow-up offers reduction of costs, a factor of value especially in times of restricted budgets for drugs modern imaging methods.

0-33 Gastrointestinal Ca.

The predictive value of preoperative levels of CEA and CA 19-9 in colorectal cancer patients receiving adjuvant therapy.

Van Dalen Arie, Behbehani A[1], Mathew A[1], Farghaly M[2], Stieber P[3], Hofman D[3], Nagel D[3], Lau-Werner U[4], Holubec L[5], Topolcan O[5], Finek J[5], Cerna M[5], Visokai V[6], Lipska L[6].
Institute of Tumour Marker Oncology, Gouda, The Netherlands, [1]Dept. of Surgery, Kuwait University, Kuwait, [2]Dept. of Surgery Adan Hospital, Kuwait, [3]Clinical Chemistry, [4]Dept. op Surgery University of Munich, Germany, [5]Dept. of Internal Medicine, University Hospital Pilsen, Czech Republic, [6]Medical School Charles University, Prague, Czech Republic.

Aims: A multicentre evaluation of the predictive value of preoperative CEA and CA 19-9 levels in colorectal patients receiving adjuvant therapy.
Methods: Two-year disease-free survival was analyzed in 485 patients.
The clinical parameters T-, and N-stage, grade, tumour site, gender and age were compared with different cut-off levels of CEA and CA 19-9.
Results: At the cut-of level of 8.4 ng/ml (CEA) and 29.0 U/ml (CA 19-9) the number of patients with elevated TM level equals patients staging pN2. These TM levels and pN2 are independent prognostic factor of 2-year DFS (multivariate analysis). The number of patients involved increases from 89 (pN2) to 157 (including CEA) and to 205 (including CEA and CA 19-9). The combined group of patients staging pN2 ***or*** an elevated TM level have a worse prognosis in developing recurrent disease (RR=3.4; PPV=46.5% and % relapse detected=66.0%)
Conclusions: Is "routine" adjuvant treatment of patients staging pN2 or with a CEA level above 8.4 ng/ml and/or a CA 19-9 level above 29.0 U/l adequate?

0-34 Gastrointestinal Ca.

Abstract not submitted.

0-35 Gastrointestinal Ca.

IGF-I receptor as a marker for prognosis and a therapeutic target in esophageal squamous cell carcinoma.

Adachi Yasushi, Imsumran A, Yamamoto H, Piao W, Shinomura Y, Lee CT, Carbone DP, Imai K
First Department of Internal Med, Sapporo Medical Univ, Sapporo (Japan) and Vanderbilt Univ Med Ctr, Nashville, TN (USA).

Aims: Insulin-like growth factor (IGF)-I receptor (IGF-Ir) signaling is required for tumorigenicity and progression of many tumors but this pathway has not been well studied as a prognostic factor or potential therapeutic factor in esophageal squamous cell carcinomas (ESCC).
Methods: In this paper, the association between the expression of IGF-II and IGF-Ir and prognosis was investigated immunohistochemically in 100 surgically resected ESCC and we assessed whether recombinant adenoviruses expressing dominant negative IGF-Ir (IGF-Ir/dn) would represent potentially effective therapeutics for ESCC.
Results: Expression of IGF-Ir and IGF-II were detected in 60% and 50% of tumors, respectively, and were associated with invasion depth, metastasis, advanced tumor stage, and recurrence. Patients with tumors expressing both IGF-Ir and IGF-II had a significantly shorter survival than those expressing neither in both single and multivariate analysis. IGF-Ir/dn suppressed proliferation and motility as well as up-regulating chemotherapy-induced apoptosis through blocking ligand-induced Akt activation.
Conclusions: We propose that detection of IGF-Ir/IGF-II in ESCC may be useful for the prediction of recurrence and poor prognosis and for selecting patients for IGF-Ir targeted therapy. The blockade of IGF-Ir, e.g. Adenovirus-IGF-Ir/dn, may be a useful anticancer therapeutic for ESCC.

0-36 Gastrointestinal Ca.

CEA and CA19-9 in patients with relapse of colorectal carcinoma.

Visokai Vladimir, Lipska L, Levy M, Kormunda S
Department of Surgery of Thomayer Teaching Hospital and the 1st Faculty of Medicine Charles University, Prague, Czech Republic

Aims: to evaluate the value of CEA and CA 19-9 in follow up in a large retrospective study
Methods: in the years 1992-2004, 1090 patients were operated for colorectal cancer, 716 of them with R0 resection and 631 followed up at the same surgical department. Relapse was diagnosed in 122 patients (20%), 74 were indicated for reoperation, in 43 second R0 resection was performed(35% resectability of relaps with 0% postoperative mortality). Both CEA and CA19-9 are known in 75 patients with relapse.
Results: at the time of relapse 61% of patients had elevation of CEA and 33% of CA19-9 . Both markers were normal in 31% of patients with relapse. One third of recurrences was diagnosed by other methods. Comparing preoperative levels of CEA with levels at the time of relapse, in 77% of patients with elevation before primary operation , the relapse was again accompanied with an elevation, in case of CA19-9 it was in 64%. In the subgroup with normal preoperative levels of CEA, 48% had normal levels of CEA during recurrence and 79% in case of CA19-9.
Conclusions: An elevation of tumor markers can be expected mainly in cases, where the monitored marker was elevated before operation.

0-37 Therapy

DNA aptamers for in vivo molecular targeted imaging and therapy

Missailidis S[1], Perkins AC[2]
[1]Chemistry Department, The Open University, Milton Keynes, MK7 6AA, UK.
[2]Medical Physics, Medical School, Uni Hospital, Nottingham, NG7 2UH, UK

Introduction: Molecular targeted therapeutics offers high target affinity, specificity and improved therapeutic potential with reduced side effects. The traditional use of antibodies has presented problems associated with production, purification, immunogenicity and size, whereas small peptides have reduced affinities and specificities. Aptamers can be generated rapidly against targets, showing a better tumour penetration, rapid uptake and clearance, thus providing effective vehicles for cytotoxic agents.
Aims: We aimed to use DNA aptamers as recognition molecules on malignant disease to generate novel targeted radiopharmaceuticals for the diagnosis and treatment of tumours.
Methods: We employed combinatorial chemistry techniques coupled with PCR to rapidly select aptamers from degenerate libraries that bind with high affinity and specificity to the protein core of the MUC1 tumour marker. The selection process was performed on affinity chromatography matrices. After ten rounds of selection and amplification, aptamers were cloned and sequenced. Post SELEX amino modifications were used to confer nuclease resistance and coupling potential. Tc-99m was used for labelling and gamma scintigraphy.
Results: Aptamers bound to MUC1 with a Kd of 5nm and high specificity, demonstrated by fluorescent microscopy on MUC1-expresing tumour cells. Using peptide coupling reactions, we have attached chelators for Tc-99m radiolabelling to the aptamers. Biodistribution studies demonstrated tumour specificity and exceptional tumour penetration. However, the small aptamer size resulted in rapid kidney uptake and excretion.
Conclusions: Higher MW constructs, including tetra-aptamer complexes, offer improved properties and better balance between tumour penetration and higher retention times. Further work is planned using Re-188 to produce a therapeutic aptamer conjugate.

0-38 Therapy

Ex vivo expansion of cord blood derived hematopoietic stem cells

Fibach Eitan
Dept. of Hematology, Hadassah University Hospital, Jerusalem, Israel

Aims: Cord blood provides an alternative source to bone marrow and peripheral blood for hematopoietic stem cell (HSC) transplantation. However, the number of such cells in cord blood limits its use to children. One approach to overcome this shortage is ex-vivo expansion. In vitro, addition of cytokines drives HSC into extensive proliferation, but their expansion is constrained by differentiation and apoptosis. We defined three mechanisms that induce these processes in HSC. (A) Oxidative stress mediated by cell free copper. (B) The action of retinoic acid derivatives present in the serum through their nuclear receptors. (C) NAD(+)-dependent class-III-histone-deacetylases (Sir2). We tested various agents with the aim to interfere with these mechanisms under conditions that favour cell proliferation, and thus expend the number of transplantation-competent HSC.
Methods: HSC, purified from cord blood by immunomagnetic beads using Ab. to the CD34 or CD133 surface Ag, were cultured in liquid medium with serum, early-acting cytokines and the tested compounds.
Results: Cellular free copper was decreased by treatment with the cell permeable chelator – tetraethylenehexamine. The retinoid effect was prevented by the retinoic acid receptor pan-antagonist - AGN 194310 and the Sir2 activity was inhibited by nicotinamide. Although these treatments did not affect, after 2-3 weeks, the total number of cells they increased significantly the number and proportion of early HSC, having the CD34+CD38- or CD34+Lin- phenotypes, which maintained long-term culture potential and transplantability in NOD/SCID mice.
Conclusions: The results suggest that these treatments could provide strategies for expending cord blood HSC for therapeutic purposes.

0-39 Therapy

Facets of low dose irradiation and the death of a tumour cell

Eriksson D[1], Sheikholvaezin A[1], Johansson L[2], Åhlström KR[3], Stigbrand Torgny[1]
[1]Departments of Immunology, [2]Radiation Physics and [3]Diagnostic Radiology, University of Umeå, S-90187 Umeå, Sweden

Aims: To elucidate mechanisms behind the cytotoxic effects mediated by low dose irradiation
Methods and Results: In response to radiation induced DNA damage, a network of signalling pathways is activated arresting the damaged cell at several different cell cycle checkpoints. We analysed low dose irradiated HeLa Hep2 cells using flowcytometry and observed aberrations in the cell cycle related check points, making it possible for these cells to enter mitosis. This premature entry into mitosis without complete reparation of radiation induced cellular damage give rise to several different mitotic aberrations like lagging chromosomes, anaphase bridges and multipolar spindles that could be detected by immunocytochemical staining of α-tubulin. These mitotic aberrations generate cells with micronuclei and also multinucleated, polyploid cells due to failure to complete cytokinesis and the cells are destined to die by this "mitotic catastrophe". At least a subgroup of these cells die due to a delayed form of apoptosis and the induction pathways have been elucidated. Both the initiator caspases 2,9,8 as well as effector caspase 3 were found to be activated after low dose radiation.
Conclusion: Mitotic catastrophe and activation of caspases belonging to both the intrinsic and extrinsic pathways are involved in the radiation induced apoptosis seen at radioimmunotheraphy.

0-40 Therapy

Monoclonal antibody (mAb) in cancer therapy, success and necessity to maintain active reseach in the field.

Mach Jean-Pierre, Cesson V, Robert B, Donda A
Department Biochemistry, Lausanne University, Switzerland

While we celebrate the 30 years'anniversary of the mAb technology discovery, by Köhler and Milstein (Nature 1975), we only now witness the broad clinical applications of mAbs in cancer therapy. Indeed, half of the mAbs, approved for clinical use are dedicated to cancer therapy and every year new mAbs, some of them radiolabeled, are approved for this application (Stern and Herrmann, 2005). Despite the success, we realize that the percentages of complete tumor remissions, are still modest and that continued research efforts are needed to make the antibody molecules (which were developed by « nature » mostly to fight virus and bacteria) more efficient in the specific destruction of malignant cells. Identification of target tumor associated antigens, often oncofetal, has been a constant goal of ISOBM members, for review (Mach J.-P. Encyclopedia Life Science, 2002, www.els.net). After many years of work on radiolabeld mAbs, our group has concentrated now on the design of a new cancer immunotherapy strategy, whereby mAbs can target on tumor cells antigenic MHC/peptide complexes and thus induce their killing by peptide specific CD8 T-lymphocytes (Donda A. et al. 2003). Similarly, B. Robert s'group showed recently that anti-tumor mAbs, coupled to the MHC class I *related* MIC-A, induce the specific killing of tumor cells by NK cells (C. Germain et al. Clin.Cancer Res. in press).

0-41 Therapy

Cord Blood Hematopoietic Stem/Progenitor Cells (SP): Biology, Transplantation and Plasticity

Arnon Nagler
Chaim Sheba Medical Center, Tel Hashomer, Israel.

Cord blood SP cells are being used for hematopoietic transplantation with encouraging results (these topics will be covered in the lecture). We, currently, asked can they be used for cardiac regeneration. SP cells were isolated from UCB of newborns by Miltenyi device. An MI model was established by permanent legation of the left anterior descending coronary artery. Fresh or ex vivo expanded SP cells were injected intramuscular (at the scar tissue), intracoronary or intravenously. The presence of human-donor cells in recipient heart was confirmed by FISH or HLA-DR immunostaining. In a pig model, the SP cells were labeled immediately prior to infusion with ^{99m}Tc and migration and homing to the infracted myocardium was assessed by gamma camera. Angiogenesis was assessed by staining for smooth muscle alpha-actin. Serial echocardiographic studies were performed at baseline and 4 weeks post treatment. Expression of VEGF and VEGF receptor RNA was examined by RT-PCR. Intravenously injection of 1.2-2x10^6 fresh CB SP cells 48h after MI resulted in prevention of LV systolic dysfunction and anterior wall thinning. HLA-DR immunostaining revealed that the human cells migrated and colonized the infarcted myocardium. Furthermore, positive HLA staining and XY signals were observed in vessel walls, suggesting differentiation of the human donor cells into cardiac vasculature.
Finally, in the pig model we could demonstrated that up to 30-40% of the CB SP cells colonized in the infarcted myocardium.

0-42 Therapy

Targeting Tumor Lectins, A Galactmannan Derivative, Shows Promising Results in Pre-Clinical and Phase I Clinical Trial in Patients with Refractory Solid Tumors.

Jyotsna F[1], Y. Abubakr[2], R. Perez[3], M. Zalupski[4], M. Pike[5], D. Platt[5], E. Zomer[5],A. Klyosov[5]
[1]Ochsner Cancer Institute, LA; [2]Florida Oncology Associates, FL; [3]Dartmouth Hitchcock Medical Center, NH; [4]University of Michigan Medical Center, MI; [5]Pro-Pharmaceuticals, Inc., MA

Aims: Galactomannan derivative (cGM, DAVANAT®) enhances 5-Fluorouracil (5-FU) in refractory tumor models. cGM interacts with galactose specific lectins, facilitating transport of 5-FU into tumor cells. These lectins on tumor surfaces, mediate cell association, tumor apoptosis and metastasis.
Methods: Clinical Phase I studies conducted to establish the safety and tolerability of escalating doses of cGM administrated with 5-FU. Additional animal studies were designed to evaluate the effect of cGM with oncotherapeutics like irinotecan, oxaliplatin and bevacizumab, simulating clinical regimens.
Results: Phase I trial of advanced metastatic patients found DAVANAT (280 mg/m^2) alone and in combination with 5-FU (500 mg/m^2) is well tolerated. Three patients had SAEs (dehydration, dyspnea and thrombocytopenia) thought to be at least possibly drug related. Of 26 patients with measurable disease, with average tumor load of over 100mm, 14 had stable, and 11 had progressive disease (RECIST). Animal models show an enhancement of anticancer activity when administrated with oncolytic or antiangiogenic agents.
Conclusions: cGM tolerability and enhancement of anticancer therapy in animal models and rate of patients' stabilization warrants further investigation of its anti-cancer benefit.

0-43 Therapy

Clinical Applications of Stem Cell Technologies

Avraham J. Treves
Cancer Research Center, Sheba Medical Center, Israel

Cell therapy is an emerging modality with increasing numbers of products and technologies under development. Stem cells are a unique population of immature cells, with potential to both replicate (self-renewal) and differentiate into different types of mature functional cells. Two types of stem cells are being studied for their tissue regenerative potential: Embryonic stem cells (ES) originating from the inner mass of the blastocyst; and adult stem cells (ASC) that populate all tissues and organs. ASC are responsible for replenishing normal tissues and regenerating damaged tissue throughout the life of the organism. Committed stem and progenitor cells differentiate into specific lineages but some ASC maintain plasticity potential and may turn into different cell lineages. Their first clinical utilization was to replace ablated bone marrow for treatment of leukemia and this modality is today the treatment of choice for many malignant and genetic hematological diseases. Numerous clinical studies are being conducted recently to treat ischemic heart muscle, using autologous bone marrow derived stem cells or muscle derived myoblasts. Emerging frontier of stem cell therapy is the treatment of injured spinal cord, but only few studies have been reported. Novel clinical applications such as treatment of liver diseases, diabetes, neurodegenerative diseases and many others, are at their pre-clinical research stage. Several technologies for ex-vivo expansion or manipulation of stem cells and tissue engineered products are under development by biotech industry and few are in clinical development.

0-44 Therapy

Adjuvant Intravesical Treatment of Superficial Urinary Bladder Cancer with Mistletoe Extract

Elsässer-Beile Ursula (1), Leiber C (1), Bühler P (1), Mengs U (2) and Wetterauer U (1)

(1) Department of Urology, Freiburg, Germany
(2) Madaus AG, Köln, Germany

Aims: Patients with superficial bladder cancer are mostly treated by transurethral tumor resection and adjuvant intravesical therapy with Bacillus Calmette-Guerin (BCG), which was shown to reduce tumor recurrence significantly. However, serious side effects of this treatment promoted the search for other immunoactive substances, which to date have failed to show the equal efficacy as BCG. Therefore, the aim of the present study was to evaluate the effect of intravesical mistletoe extract (ME) with respect to tolerability and recurrence rate.
Methods: In a phase I/II clinical trial an aqueous ME, standardized to mistletoe lectin, was administered intravesically to 24 patients with urinary bladder cancer of the stages pTa G2 (n=14) and pT1 G2 (n=10). After transurethral resection each patient received 6 instillations at weekly intervals with 50 ml of the extract with mistletoe lectin concentrations between 10 ng/ml and 5,000 ng/ml. A local historical control group consisted of 18 patients with pTa G2 (n=5) and pT1 G2 (n=13) tumors that were treated with 6 BCG instillations after transurethral resection.
Results: The tolerability of the ME was very good. None of the patients had local or systemic side effects. Within the observation time of 12 months, the patients treated with ME showed a recurrence rate of 8/24 (33%). In the BCG treated group the recurrence rate was 5/18 (28 %) and therefore similar in both groups.
Conclusions: Standardized ME could be a potential alternative adjuvant therapy for superficial bladder cancer.

0-45 Therapy

Cardio-Specific Enzymes Assessment at Heart Failure Patients Treated with Radiotherapy

Holubec Luboš, Topol an O., Salvet J., Svoboda T., Svobodová Š., Fínek J Dept. of Oncology University Hospital Pilsen and Central Isotopic Lab., Charles University Pilsen, Czech Republic

Aims: The aim of the study is to assess changes of cardio-specific markers levels (BNP, NT-pro BNP, and Seristra) in patients treated with radiotherapy and to evaluate whether these markers would be useful for monitoring of clinically manifested heart failure in patients treated with anticancer therapy.
Methods: Cardio-specific enzymes (BNP /Chemiluminiscence, Beckman/, NT pro BNP /ELISA, Biomedica/ and Seristra /Immunoluminiscence, Brahms/) were assessed prior and after radiation (+/- 5 days). The study group involved 37 patients treated with radiotherapy (29 breast cancer patients, 5 oesophagus cancer patients, 2 lung cancer patients and 1 Hodgkin's disease patient). This group involved 20 patients with a negative history of cardiovascular diseases and 17 patients with a positive history of cardiovascular diseases (arterial hypertension, ischemic heart disease, heart failure, and arrhythmia).
Results: Patients with a positive history of cardiovascular diseases performed significantly increased levels of BNP after radiotherapy compared to the pre-radiation levels ($p > 0.001$). 30% patients (11/37) performed pathological values of BNP (above100 pg/mL). These values were suspicious for cardiac insufficiency. NT- pro BNP and Seristra values did not perform any statistically significant differences.
Conclusions: BNP in patients with a positive history of cardiovascular diseases, seems to be a promising marker of cardiovascular disease for radiotherapy monitoring.

0-46 Therapy

Abstract not submitted.

0-47 Breast Ca.

Relationship between Akt1 phosphorylation and VEGF, its receptors and Bcl-2 protein levels in human breast cancer

Elena S.Gershtein, A.M.Scherbakov, O.A.Anurova, N.E.Kushlinsky.
Russian N.N.Blokhin Cancer Research Center, Moscow, Russia.

Aims: The aim was to explore the role of activated protein kinase B (pAkt1) in clinical breast cancer in relation to the state of VEGF-signaling system and an antiapoptotic marker Bcl-2 involved in an important interplay with PI3K/Akt pathway while regulating breast cancer growth, survival, hormone, drug, and radiosensitivity.
Methods: pAkt1 level was evaluated in a series of 46 breast cancer and adjacent mammary gland samples by a direct «PathScan™ Phospho-Akt1 (Ser473) Sandwich ELISA Kit». VEGF, sVEGFR1, sVEGFR2, and Bcl-2 levels were measured in the same samples by standard ELISA kits.
Results: 48% of the tumors had an increased pAkt level as compared to adjacent mammary gland. Frequency of pAkt1 elevation was positively associated with tumor malignancy grade (γ=0.48; $p<0.05$), and no significant associations with other clinical-pathologic factors were observed. pAkt1 level was increased in ER positive tumors as compared to ER negative ($p<0.05$), but it was twice as frequently increased in PgR negative as in PgR positive tumors (59% vs. 30%; $p<0.01$). VEGF, sVEGFR1, sVEGFR2, and Bcl-2 were all increased in 73-85% of the tumors, but no associations with the majority of clinical-biological factors were found. Frequency of pAkt1 elevation in tumor tissue was positively associated only with sVEGFR2 level (γ=0.33; $p<0.05$).
Conclusions: In clinical breast cancer activation of Akt1 kinase is not clearly associated with the state of the VEGF signaling system or Bcl-2 expression, but is related to steroid hormone receptor status.
The study was supported by RFBR grant 03-03-32111.

0-48 Breast Ca.

Secretoglobins: Potential Markers for Breast Cancer.

Duffy MJ, Culleton J, Flanagan L, O'Brien N.
Dept. of Nuclear Medicine, St Vincent's University Hospital, Dublin.

Aims: To study the distribution and potential significance of MGA and LPB in breast cancer.
The secretoglobin supergene family encode low molecular weight secreted proteins. The human members include mammaglobin A (MGA), mammaglobin B (MGB), (also known as lipophilin C), and lipophilin B (LPB), (also known as BU101). Two of these secretoglobins, ie, MGA and LPB are expressed relatively specifically in breast tissue and are thus potential markers for breast cancer.
Methods: MGA and LPB were measured at mRNA level using RT-PCR. MGA protein was also determined by Western blotting.
Results: Using RT-PCR, MGA mRNA was detected in 4/12 (33%) normal breast tissues, in 57/102 (56%) of breast carcinomas but in none out of 11 non-breast tissues. In contrast, LPB mRNA was detected in 9/12 (75%) of normal breast tissues, in 68/102 (67%) of breast carcinomas and in 4/11 (36%) non-breast tissues. LPB thus appears to be a more sensitive but less specific marker for breast cancer than MGA. Using western blotting, MGA protein was found to exist in 2 main forms, migrating with molecular masses of approximately 18 and 25 kDa. An inverse relationship was found between the 25 kDa form of MGA and both tumor grade and proliferation rate. On the other hand, a positive correlation was found between this form of MGA and ER.
Conclusions: These findings suggest that the presence of MGA in breast cancer is likely to reflect favourable prognosis and also possibly predict response to hormone therapy. The challenge now is to develop serum-based assays for MGA and LPB.

0-49 Breast Ca.

The effect of non-tumor parameters on the detection of metatasis in sentinel lymph node biopsies.

Nap Marius
Dept. of Pathology, Atrium medical center Heerlen, The Netherlands.

Aims: We wanted to be informed about some qualitative aspects of our sentinel lymph node(SLN) biopsy program in breast cancer.
Methods: We performed an observational study, including all available parameters on SLN biopsy procedures.
Results: We analyzed our data from 2000 until now. The % of patients, eligible for SLN biopsy was 60%. However, a decrease from 40% to 20% was found for SLN with metastasis. We noticed that after an initial increase of larger metastasis, a plateau was reached but than the % of SLN metastasis > 2 mm diminished. At the same time the % < 2 mm showed a relative increase from 10% towards 30%. There was no relation with T stage.
In the same period the relative number of axillary lymph node metastasis, proven by FNA, increased from 2% towards 25%. This change coincided with the arrival of a radiologist with strong FNA skills. The recognition of the successful FNA procedure resulted in a concentration of requests for axillary FNA, done by radiologists, from 20% in 2000 towards 80% in 2004.
Conclusions: These observations illustrate that reduction in size of metastatic tumor in SLN not necessarily means breast cancer has changed. The recognition and acceptance of human experience appears to be an important factor that may introduce a bias if not noticed.

0-50 Breast Ca.

Abstract not submitted.

0-51 Breast Ca.

PATHOLOGY AS A BRIDGE BETWEEN RESEARCH AND CLINICAL PRACTICE

Niki J. Agnantis,
Pathology Dep.,University of Ioannina Medical School, Ioannina, Greece

Anatomic Pathology has come a long way since the time that Morgagni encouraged the postmortem search for the cause and nature of disease. During this long course the histological techniques have been continuously improving and Pathologists have been incorporating a variety of methods in their every-day practice, making diagnosis more refined and definite. In the last decades this improvement has been complemented by cytologic and molecular methods, expanding the horizons of Pathology from gross specimens to DNA.
Advances in facing cancer range widely, from basic research designed to understand the molecular causes of cancer, through the application of this knowledge for the patients' benefit. Both basic and clinical research, the latter being dependent on the former, are now developing at a fast pace. The particular challenge in cancer is:
1. To discover the molecular abnormalities that dictate each malignant growth
2. To use this information in order to understand the process of malignancy
and, based on these data,
3.To develop more rational and effective approaches for diagnosis and treatment.
Pathology is the discipline that acts as a bridge between Clinical Medicine and Basic Sciences. All novel molecular Pathology techniques are necessary, but they should be applied with caution. They should be critically appraised and analyzed in detail regarding cost/benefit, in order to contribute the most to patient care. For achieving this goal the close collaboration between Clinicians, Pathologists and Basic Researchers is necessary.

0-52 Breast Ca.

Prospective evaluation of serum tumor markers (CEA, CA 15.3 AND HER-2/neu) as prognostic factors in patients with locoregional BREAST CA

Rafael, Molina, JM. Auge, X. Filella, G. Zanon, J. Pahisa, M. Muñoz, B. Farrus.
Laboratory of Clinical Biochemistry, Hospital Clinic, Medical School. Barcelona. Spain.

Aims: To evaluate CEA,CA 15.3 and HER-2/neu as prognostics factors in breast cancer.
Methods: HER-2/neu ,an oncoprotein marker, CEA and CA 15.3 were prospectively studied in the sera of 753 untreated patients with breast cancer diagnosed between 1995 and 2003.
Results: Abnormal HER-2/neu levels (>15 ng/ml) were found in 8%, CEA (>5 ng/ml) in 11,8% and CA 15.3 (>30 U/ml) in 16,1% of the 753 patients. HER-2/neu serum levels were only related to HER-2/neu in tissue (420 patients), with significantly higher concentrations in patients with over-expression in tissue. All tumor markers (HER-2/neu only in patients with over-expression in tissue) were correlated with tumor size, TNM and nodal involvement. Univariate analysis (mean follow-up 8,8 years) showed that CEA, CA 15.3 and HER-2/neu (in those patients with overexpression in tissue) were prognostic factors with significantly shorter disease free survival (DFS) and overall survival (OS) in patients with pretreatment tumor marker positivity. Multivariate analysis (723 patients) in DFS and in OS showed that nodal, CEA, histological grade, tumor size and ER but not, menopausal status, histology, CA 15.3, HER-2/neu, PgR, adjuvant treatment, p53 (345 patients) or HER-2/neu in tissue are independent prognostic factors. It is interesting to indicate that using simultaneously all three tumor markers, recurrence was found in 10% of node negative patients with all three tumor markers negative in contrast to 58% of recurrence in those patients with one or more tumor marker positivity.
Conclusions: In summary, tumor markers are useful, cheap and reproducible tools in prognosis.

0-53 Breast Ca.

Male Breast Cancer

Roisman Isaac[1], Lifshitz .I[2], Raphaeli .G[3], Klem .O[4], Goldmann .I[5], Bitterman .A[5], Kovacs .Z[5]
[1] Horev Medical Center, Haifa; [2] Kupat Holim Meuchedet, Jerusalem; [2] Hadassah Medical Center, Jerusalem; [4] Kupat Holim Meuchedet, Haifa; [5] Carmel Medical Center, Haifa, ISRAEL

Aims: To review male breast cancer, new modalities of detection and updated treatment.
Breast cancer in men is a rare disease, accounting for approximately 1% of all breast cancer patients. Although the epidemiologic literature regarding female breast cancer is extensive, relatively little is known about the etiology of male breast cancer (MBC).
Methods: Clinical parameters were compared to genetics and markers.
Results: Major genetic factors associated with an increased risk of breast cancer for men include BRCA2 mutations, which are believed to account for the majority of inherited breast cancer in men, Klinefelter syndrome, and a positive family history. Suspected genetic factors include AR gene mutations, CYP17 polymorphism, Cowden syndrome, and CHEK2.
Between 2001 - 2004 we treated 43 men with breast cancer. One patient had bilateral breast cancer. The mean age was 64. 89% of the patients presented with breast mass. 77.3%, as in the literature, were invasive duct carcinoma, 68% were in stage I, and 11% were in stage IV. Modified radical mastectomy was the operation all the patients underwent. Five year survival was achieved in stage I -in 73%, stage II -in 42%, stage III – in 26%. We shall present in details our findings and discuss the literature.
Conclusions: Modified radical mastectomy followed by a supplement of updated medication,is the treatment of choice in male breast cancer.

0-54 Breast Ca.

A web-based method for external validation of survival estimates based on a nationwide series of patients with breast cancer

Lundin Johan[a], Lehtimäki T[a], Lundin M[a], Isola J[b], Joensuu H[a]
[a]Department of Oncology,University of Helsinki, Helsinki, Finland
[b] Institute of Medical Technology, University of Tampere, Tampere, Finland

Aims: The purpose of this study was to develop a method for external validation of survival estimates based on a Finnish nationwide breast cancer series.
Methods: A previously described web-based survival estimation system www.finprog.org, allows the user to enter information on prognostic factors, and instantly obtain a survival curve based on cases in the database with a matching prognostic factor profile. The source for the survival estimates is the FinProg breast cancer database (n= 2,842). Functionality for dynamic validation of the survival estimates was added to the system. The validation algorithm was tested on data from the population-based SEER program in the US, as well as an independent breast cancer series from Finland.
Results: When the user of the web-based system selects the "Validate" option, a comparison of the FinProg estimate with a corresponding survival curve based on the external data is automatically performed and a logrank test calculated. A number of prognostic profiles for lymph node status, tumor size, histologic grade and hormone-receptor status, adjusted for age at diagnosis were generated. Forty-four of the 54 (81%) example profiles did not significantly differ in the external data and were thus considered to be validated.
Conclusions: Validated case-match models could provide quantitative survival estimates to be used in the decision-making process concerning treatment of patients with breast cancer.

0-55 AFP

Biological properties of alfa-fetoprotein and alpha-fetoprotein receptors

José Uriel
CNRS BP8. 94801-Villejuif. France

The ability to bind and to internalize AFP, characteristic of fetal cells, may be resumed in many tumor cells of varied origin as well as in some normal adult cells undergoing growth and differentiation. This ability results from the expression at the cell surface of specific receptors to the protein . Many studies have demonstrated the presence of AFP receptors in human and animals malignant cells . The expression of AFP receptors is often concomitant with the expression of the AFP gene and strongly suggests the activation of an AFP/AFP receptor autocrine pathway in these cells. The activation appears transient for normal cells, while it changes to constitutive- in malignant ones.

The biological functions of AFP and AFP receptors have not been completely elucidated. Past and recent work on the role of AFP as a carrier protein of fatty acids (FA) strongly suggests that the entry of FA in living cells undergoing growth and/or differentiation is a function of unbound, free FA but appears to be regulated by the carrier protein which, through its interaction with specific AFP receptors at the cell surface, facilitates and enhances the uptake of FA. This activity of the autocrine system AFP/AFP-receptors may have considerable patho-physiological impact since FA exert structural and metabolic functions which are crucial for cell growth and survival of tumor cells It also offers the possibility of biomedical applications, namely cancer diagnosis.

0-56 AFP

The use of recombinant human alpha-fetoprotein for treatment of autoimmune central nervous system inflammation

Irony-Tur Sinai M.[1], Grigoriadis N.[2], Abramsky O.[1], and Brenner T[1].
[1]Department of Neurology and Agnes Ginges Center for Neurogenetics, Hadassah Hebrew University Medical Center, Jerusalem, Israel, [2]Aristotle University, Thessaloniki Greece.

Aims: Determine mode of action of onco-fetal glycoprotein alpha-fetoprotein (rhAFP) on the autoimmune-inflammatory process in the experimental model of Multiple Sclerosis (MS).
Background: AFP is an immunomodulating, embryo-specific glycoprotein. Clinical remissions during the second half of pregnancy have been described in several autoimmune diseases such as MS Rheumatoid Arthritis and Myasthenia Gravis, and are attributed to the immunosuppressive effect of AFP.
Methods: Following the recent development of a novel technology based on the secretion of rhAFP in transgenic goat milk, we tested this preparation in the mouse model of experimental autoimmune encephalomyelitis (EAE). Clinical outcome, T-cell reactivity and central nervous system (CNS) damage were evaluated.
Results: Both goat-derived rhAFP preparations and cord blood AFP caused marked suppression of EAE. CNS tissue from AFP-treated mice showed a pronounced reduction in degree of inflammation, axonal loss and injury. AFP exerted a broad immunomodulating activity, influencing the various populations of immune cells. The activity of T and B-cells from treated mice was significantly reduced, and the expression of MHC class II and .chemokine receptor CCR5 were down regulated.
Conclusions: Our observations further support the role of the embryo-specific glycoprotein AFP in amelioration of experimental autoimmune diseases.

0-57 New markers

RECAF - A New Tumor Marker

Ricardo Moro
BioCurex Inc. Vancouver, Canada (rmoro@biocurex.com).

The receptor for AFP (RECAF) is used to incorporate fatty acids and other molecules carried by AFP into fetal cells from most organs and tissues. RECAF is not expressed by normal adult cells but it reappears in cancer cells thus acting as a broad spectrum oncofetal antigen. The AFP binding site on RECAF is the glycan portion of several soluble and membrane glycoproteins. Antibodies against the RECAF glycan can be used for detecting cancer cells by immuno-histology on paraffin or frozen tissue sections, as well as for immuno-cytology on smears.

We have also developed a RIA to detect RECAF in serum and we have obtained high sensitivity values (with 95% specificity) for the following cancers: Breast (93%), cervical (86%), colorectal (75%), leukemia and lymphomas (80%), lung (94%), melanoma (80%), ovarian (96%), prostate (88%) and stomach (90%). Most benign lesions of the prostate (BPH) or the breast have serum RECAF values similar to those of normal individuals thus offering very good discrimination between benign tumors and malignancy.

Anti-RECAF antibodies or AFP itself can also be used for targeting cancer cells with radioactivity for tumor imaging and with mercurial compounds to selectively kill cancer cells. *In-vitro* experiments show 100% killing in a variety of cancers with 5-15% death of normal cells. The implications for cancer therapy and management are discussed.

0-58 New markers

Human Tissue Kallikreins

Eleftherios P. Diamandis
Clinical Biochemistry, Mount Sinai Hospital, University Health Network and Toronto Medical Laboratories and Department of Laboratory Medicine and Pathobiology, University of Toronto

Aims: Kallikreins are 15 serine proteases encoded by a cluster of genes located on human chromosome 19q13.4. Until 5 years ago, the human kallikrein gene locus was thought to consist of only 3 genes. It is now established that this family includes 15 genes which encode for homologous serine proteases, are secreted and hormonally regulated. The function of these newly discovered enzymes is largely unknown.

Results: Kallikreins are found in large amounts in endocrine/regulated tissues such as breast, prostate and testis. Many of these genes are coordinately regulated and are found in groups in many tissues.It has been speculated that at least some of them participate in cascade enzymatic pathways similar to those of coagulation, fibrinolysis, digestion, etc. A significant body of evidence indicates that kallikreins are involved in extracellular matrix remodeling and regeneration, receptor activation, hormone processing, etc. It is now clear that many members of the kallikrein are dysregulated in many forms of cancer and especially, ovarian cancer. Convincing data show that these enzymes, measured in either serum, tissue extracts and other biological fluids carry diagnostic and prognostic information.

Conclusions: Kallikrein research is now shifting from gene discovery to protein function and dysregulation in various diseases. The better understanding of the role of this proteolytic system in physiology and pathobiology will likely lead to therapies which are targeting these enzymes through specific inhibitors.

0-59 New markers

5-Aminolevulinic acid stimulated protoporphyrin IX:
A sensitive marker for photodynamic detection of breast cancer

Walt Heinrich
Dept. of OB/GYN, University Hospital, Zurich, Switzerland

Aims: Photodynamic detection of tumours by means of 5-aminolevulinic acid (5-ALA)-induced protoporphyrin IX (PpIX) is of increasing interest in oncology. Regarding breast cancer, we here present preclinical and clinical data, underlining an upcoming role of this marker.
Methods: The heme substrate 5-ALA (200 mg/kg) was administered to mouse strains that develop mammary tumours of various histological subtypes and metastatic potential. 20 human patients with breast cancer received 30 mg 5-ALA per kg bodyweight orally 3 h prior to surgery. In both human patients and mice malignant areas were evidenced by red fluorescence when the tumours were directly illuminated with blue light at 405 nm.
Results: Mouse mammary tumours at the stage of *ductal carcinoma in situ* as small as 1mm in diameter were detectable as well as primary tumours and metastases. They showed consistent and rapid PpIX accumulation compared to the normal surrounding tissues. Similarly, this was the case in human mammary tumour tissues and in diseased sentinel lypmh nodes.
Conclusions: Enhanced PpIX synthesis, stimulated by 5-ALA, is a good marker for early tumourigenic processes in the mammary gland as evidenced experimentally. We suggest that photodynamic detection of tumour margins and of metastasized sentinel lymph nodes with 5-ALA for breast tumours should be further investigated in both the experimental model and in human patients.

0-60 New markers

Follow up of patients with carcinoid tumors: Combination of Chromogranin A and NT-proBNP

Bonfrer Johannes MG[1], Korse CM[1], Taal BG[2]
[1]Dept. of Clin. Chem.and [2]Medical Oncology, The Netherlands Cancer Institute – Amsterdam

Aims: 5HIAA is used in carcinoid tumors. We evaluated the impact of changing marker to Chromogranin A (CgA). Carcinoid heart disease (CHD) occurs in 20-70 % of the patients with carcinoid tumors. We evaluated natriuretic peptides (ANP and NT-proBNP) in the diagnosis of CHD.
Methods: 5HIAA was measured using an ELISA (DRG), CgA- by RIA (Cis). The patients- 18 males and 19 females. To establish a reference value for CgA we collected serum in 90 healthy volunteers.
Results: The inter C.V. for 5HIAA was on average 25%, and for CgA 6.5%. Reference values (95%) were 40 mmol/24hrs for 5HIAA and 120 µg/l for CgA. No significant difference was found in marker concentrations related to age or gender. The relation between markers and 5 life parameters were calculated after log transformation using a linear model with random coefficients. It was shown that a change of 5HIAA did not correlate with any parameter but CgA changes were significantly related to 2. CHD was found in 8/32 patients (25%). All CHD patients had symptoms of the carcinoid syndrome compared to 67% of the non-CHD patients (p=0.08). Patients with CHD had elevated NT-proBNP levels. Degree of dilatation of right atrium or ventricle was significantly associated with higher levels of NT -proBNP. Thickening of the tricuspid valve and degree of regurgitation were accompanied by significantly higher levels of both natriuretic peptides. Although not significant, a trend for a better survival was observed in patients with normal NT-proBNP values.
Conclusions: The CgA assay can replace the 5HIAA assay as a marker for follow up of patients with carcinoid tumors. NT-proBNP can be used as a reliable diagnostic marker for CHD. The combined measurement of CgA and NT-proBNP in carcinoid patients is recommended.

0-61 New markers

PROGNOSTIC AND PREDICTIVE IMPORTANCE OF THYMIDINE KINASE (TK)

Topolcan O., Holubec L.jr., Kausitz J., Svobodova S., Votava T., Cerna Z. and Finek J.

Medical Faculty of Charles University , Pilsen, and Faculty Hospitals in Pilsen and 1st Medical Faculty of Charles University, Prague.Czech Republic

Aims: To evaluate prognostic and predictive importance of TK levels in solid tumours and hemathological malignancies.
Methods: TK was measured by radioreceptor analysis (RRA). Serum levels of TK were measured in 691 persons divided into following groups: 280 controls (100- healthy, 140- inflammatory diseases, 40- immune diseases).Cancer patients: 200 patients with solid tumors (100 breast ca., 100CRC)- prior surgery and during follow-up, 181 hemathological malignancies (37 children with acute leukemia, 68 Hodgkin lymphoma, 36 non-Hodgkin lymphoma, 40 plasmocyte myeloma), TK levels of CRC during adjuvant or palliative chemotherapy-5-FU (30 patients).
Results: In the control group elevated serum levels of Tk were found in patients with viral infection or in patients with immunology diseases. Average sensitivity of TK at recommended 95% specificity for solid tumors was 30% for primary diagnostics, the highest values were observed for non-differentiated cancers. Sensitivities during follow-up were significantly higher for recurrent disease (60-70%) and therefore potentially useful for diagnostics. Sensitivities of this test for hematology malignancies were depended on the type of malignancy. The highest sensitivity was achieved in acute children leukemia (SN 87%), in other types of hematological malignancies were sensitivities within the range of 30-54%. Serum levels of TK in acute children leukemia were extremely high (between 300-800 IU/L). In case of adjuvant or palliative chemotherapy the dynamics of TK levels was corresponding to the effect of therapy.
Conclusions: TK has been confirmed to be a proper tumor marker for hematology malignancies. It seems to be only a secondary tumor marker for breast cancer and colorectal cancer. But it seems to be an optimal marker for therapy control. The interpretation of these tests must be performed only together with the clinical status evaluation. In case of elevated results it is necessary to exclude any viral complications.

0-62 EGTM

CA 125 in Ovarian Cancer: European Group on Tumor Marker (EGTM) Guidelines For Clinical Use.

M J Duffy, J M Bonfrer, J Kulpa, G J S Rustin, G Soletormos, GC Torre, M K Tuxen, M Zwirner, St Vincent's Hospital, Dublin. Netherlands Cancer Institute, Amsterdam. Oncological Center, Krakow. Mount Vernon Centre for Cancer Treatment, Middlesex. Hillerod Hospital, Copenhagen. Azienda Oespedaliera, Pietra Ligure, Herlev Hospital, Copenhagen. University of Tubingen, Tubingen.

Aims: The aim of this article is to provide guidelines for the routine clinical use of CA 125 in patients with ovarian cancer.
Methods: A review of the literature relating to CA 125 in ovarian cancer was carried out.
Results: Lack of sensitivity and lack of specificity preclude the use of CA 125 in the detection of early ovarian cancer. At present therefore, CA 125 either alone or in combination with other modalities, cannot be recommended for screening for ovarian cancer in asymptomatic women outside the context of a randomised controlled trial. Preoperative levels in postmenopausal women however, may aid the differentiation of benign and malignant pelvic masses. Serial levels during chemotherapy for ovarian cancer are useful for assessing response to treatment. Although serial monitoring following initial chemotherapy can lead to the early detection of recurrent disease, the clinical value of this lead-time is unclear.
Conclusions: CA 125 is the ovarian cancer marker against which new markers for this malignancy should be judged.

0-63 EGTM

Tumor markers in malignant melanoma – European Group on Tumor Markers guidelines (first draft).

1Hansson L, 2Hauschild A, 3Bonfrer JMG, 4Duffy J, 5Einarsson R
1Akademiska Laboratory, Akademiska Hospital, Uppsala, Sweden
2 Department of Dermatology, University of Kiel, Germany
3 Netherlands Cancer Institute, Amsterdam, the Netherlands
4 St. Vincents Hospital, Dublin , Ireland
5 CanAg Diagnostics, Gothenburg, Sweden

The incidences of malignant melanoma vary markedly. The highest incidence, 70/100000, is among Caucasians in Queensland, Australia. The incidence in Sweden has increased 2.7 times during the last 30 years. However, the prognosis has been steadily increased during the last decades.
Different markers have been examined during the last years; S100B, MIA, LDH, cytokines, angiogenesis factors, and metabolites of melanin synthesis. Of all these, S100B is at the moment the most widely used marker. The diagnostic sensitivity of serum S100B in patients with stage I and II malignant melanoma are low. But in advanced tumor stages, the proportion of melanoma patients who have elevated serum S100B increases, indicating micro- or macro-metastases. Especially in metastatic melanoma, elevation of S100B has been associated with shorter overall survival and thus S100B is of prognostic value in the different clinical stages of malignant melanoma. The available data on monitoring treatment justify the conclusion that circulating S100B has a clear relationship to tumor mass and can be expected to increase in excess of the normal limit when metastasis occurs.
Recommendations are discussed for the routine clinical use of serum markers in the management of patients with malignant melanoma.

0-64 EGTM

Biological Variation of Total Prostate-Specific Antigen: A Survey of Published Estimates and Consequences for Clinical Practice

Sölétormos György, Semjonow A, Sibley P, Lamerz R, Hyltoft Petersen P, Albrecht W, et al. on behalf of the EGTM.
Department of Clinical Biochemistry, Hillerød Hospital, Denmark.

Aims: To determine whether a single result of tPSA can be used confidently to guide the need for prostate biopsy, and by how much serial tPSA measurements need to differ to be significant. The EGTM investigated both the magnitude and impact of biological variation on single, the mean of replicate, and serial tPSA measurements.
Methods: The survey yielded 27 studies of which estimates for tPSA's biological variation could be derived from 12.
Results: The mean biological variation is 20% in the concentration range of 0.1–20 µg/L for men over 50 years old. The biological variation means that the one–sided 95% confidence interval (CI) for a single tPSA result is approximately 33%. Three replicate samples with one analysis on each narrow the one–sided 95% CI for the mean concentration to approximately 20% and facilitate decision on prostate biopsy. During monitoring of serial measurements the change needed for significance is approximately 50% ($P < 0.05$).
Conclusions: The biological variation of tPSA has implications for screening, diagnosis, and monitoring. Single measurements may not be sufficiently precise for screening and diagnosis. Replicate samples and calculation of the mean concentration may improve precision. Monitoring of tPSA requires an estimate of the significance of the change (Clin Chem 2005; 51:1342-51).

0-65 EGTM

Multicenter EGTM study on the evaluation of the diagnostic capacity of ProGRP in lung cancer

Stieber Petra*, Barak V*[3], Kulpa J*[6], Molina R*[7], Holdenrieder S, Hatz R[1], Schalhorn A[2], Biran H[4], Heching N[5], Nisman B[3], Peretz T[3], Filella X[7], Auge JM[7]
EGTM (European Group on Tumor Markers)*, Inst of Clin Chem, Dept of Surgery[1], Med. Dept III[2], University of Munich, Germany; Dept of Oncology, Hadassah Univ Hosp, Jerusalem[3], Sheibe Inst of Oncology, Kaplan Hospital, Rehovot[4], Dept of Oncology, Sourasky Medical Center, Tel-Aviv[5], Israel; Dept of Clin Biochem, Oncological Center Cracow Division, Cracow, Poland[6]; Bioquimica Clinica, Hospital Clinic, Barcelona, Spain[7]

Aims: ProGRP was described within the last years to be a serological biomarker with diagnostic capacity for small cell lung cancer. To establish reliable data on a large number of lung cancer patients resulting from various oncological centers, members of the lung cancer focus group within the EGTM started a multicentric evaluation. After a period of 2 years, the ProGRP data achieved were pooled and the efficacy of ProGRP to establish diagnosis of small cell lung cancer was evaluated.
Methods: In total we measured ProGRP in serum samples of 362 patients with benign lung diseases and 1474 untreated patients with lung cancer, among them 900 suffering from non small cell lung cancer (NSCLC) and 444 suffering from small cell lung cancer (SCLC). ProGRP (pg/ml) was measured in each center using the ELISA from ALSI (Japan; European distributor IBL, Hamburg, Germany).
Results: The medians of ProGRP in benign lung diseases ranged between 15 and 25 pg/ml, 95th percentile between 40 and 50 pg/ml. In NSCLC ProGRP medians ranged between 18 and 28 pg/ml, 95th percentile between 50 and 300 pg/ml. In SCLC medians were from 240 to 320 pg/ml, 95th percentiles from 3500 to 8000 pg/ml.
Conclusions: In this multicentric evaluation ProGRP was confirmed to possess a high specificity and sensitivity for small cell lung cancer.

0-66 EGTM

Tumor markers in breast cancer – European Group on Tumor Markers (EGTM) Recommendations

Rafael Molina ([a]), V.Barak ([b]), A.van Dalen ([c]), M. J. Duffy ([d]), R. Einarsson ([e]), M. Gion ([f]), H. Goike ([g]), R. Lamerz ([h]), M. Nap ([i]), G. Sölétormos ([j]), P. Stieber ([k]). EGTM Breast Cancer Guideline Group

Recommendations are presented for the routine clinical use of serum and tissue-based markers in the diagnosis and management of patients with breast cancer. Their low sensitivity and specificity preclude the use of serum markers such as the MUC-1 mucin glycoproteins (CA15.3, BR27.29 etc) and carcinoembryonic antigen (CEA) in the diagnosis of early breast cancer. However, preoperatively elevated levels of either CA 15-3 or CEA are associated with adverse outcome in patients with breast cancer, and EGTM recommends their measurement in combination with established prognostic factors. Likewise serial measurement of these markers in patients without evidence of disease after the radical treatment of the primary tumor, are useful in the early detection of recurrent disease, mainly in patients with distant metastases. Serial tumor marker determination in patients with advanced disease are useful in disease monitoring and in the evaluation of treatment efficiency. Of the tissue-based markers measurement of estrogen and progesterone receptors is mandatory in the selection of patients for treatment with hormone therapy while HER-2 is essential in selecting patients with advanced breast cancer for treatment with Herceptin (Trastuzumab). Urokinase plasminogen activator (uPA) and PAI-1 are recently validated prognostic markers for lymph node-negative breast cancer patients.

0-67 Guidelines

Guidelines for Tumor Markers: Closing the Guideline Practice Gap

Sturgeon Catharine
Department of Clinical Biochemistry, Royal Infirmary of Edinburgh, Edinburgh, UK

There is increasing pressure to provide health care based on "best practice". This is particularly true in cancer medicine, where diagnostic procedures are often invasive, and therapy expensive. Increasing interest in the use of tumour markers in the clinical management of cancer patients has encouraged the development of guidelines by local, national and international groups such as the European Group for Tumour Markers (EGTM) in Europe and the National Academy of Clinical Biochemistry (NACB) in the United States.

While their production may be commendable, guidelines are only useful if well publicised, readily implemented, and widely adopted. Establishing whether this is the case is difficult, but some indication can be obtained through carefully designed local and national audit projects. Surveys carried out through external quality assessment schemes also provide a unique means of assessing practice and confirming trends. Such surveys suggest that over the last ten years the quality of tumour marker services in the United Kingdom has been maintained or improved, with better appreciation of the importance of the care required in the preanalytical, analytical and post-analytical phases of analysis.

Much has already been accomplished in improving the effective use of tumour markers by introduction of guidelines, but further narrowing of the gap between theory and practice remains a challenge.

0-68 Guidelines

Suggestions for Guidelines to Design and Conduct Clinically Relevant Tumor Marker Trials

Sölétormos György, Hayes DF, Sturgeon C, Hyltoft Petersen P, Semjonow A, Gion M, Barak V, Duffy MJ, Sibley P, Lamerz R.
Department of Clinical Biochemistry, Hillerød Hospital, Denmark.

Aims: The aims of the presentation are to provide suggestions for a set of guidelines for designing clinical tumor marker trials.
Methods: Literature survey of original papers, reviews as well as current guidelines.
Results: It remains a paradox that tumor marker measurements are recommended by regulatory agencies, manufacturers, scientific societies, and several research groups. However, there are no generally accepted guidelines describing how clinical tumor marker trials should be designed, conducted, evaluated, and presented.
Conclusions: Even though tumor markers have been used for screening, diagnosis, and monitoring of malignant diseases for approximately two decades they have been impeded by that fact that the users, hospital departments, specialists, and general practitioners, have difficulties interpreting single, replicate, and serial measurements. Consequently, the use of tumor markers is frequently controversial and they have not obtained a solid position in clinical decision making and patient management.

0-69 CRC

Tissue Inhibitor of Metalloproteinases-1 (TIMP-1) as Tumor Marker in Colorectal Cancer

Sørensen, Nanna M[1], Blincko S[2], Weerakoon A[2], Dinsmore EJ[2], Lally JP[2], Rogers BC[2], Christensen IJ[3], Jensen V[1], Brünner N[1], Nielsen HJ[3], Dowell B[4], Davis G[4].
1 Department of Veterinary Pathobiology, Royal Veterinary and Agricultural University, Denmark.
2 Abbott Diagnostics Division, Abbott Laboratories, Dartford, UK.
3 Department of Surgical Gastroenterology, Hvidovre Hospital, Denmark.
4 Abbott Diagnostics Division, Abbott Laboratories, Abbott Park, IL, USA.

It has previously been shown that up-regulation of plasma TIMP-1 is associated with shorter patient survival. Furthermore, TIMP-1 measurements have been found to be useful in the early detection of patients with colorectal (CRC) cancer. To date, no tumor marker has been recommended as screening marker in CRC.
Aims: To develop an optimized analytic platform for plasma TIMP-1 measurements, aiming at increased sensitivity and specificity for early CRC detection.
Methods: A total of 20 anti-TIMP-1 monoclonal antibodies (mAbs) were tested as either capture or detectors in a chemiluminescence immunoassay format. Five mAb pair combinations were selected and measurements of TIMP-1 levels in non-cancerous and cancerous plasma specimens were obtained. Based on this testing a final assay format was chosen for further validation.
Results: The clinical results demonstrate that this new assay format has statistical discrimmination equivalent to our initial in-house polyclonal antibody /mAb TIMP-1 assay. In addition, the new assay had high reproducibility, good recovery, linearity and high specificity.
Conclusions: We have developed a new validated TIMP-1 assay format, which showed superiority to our previous in-house assay with regard to reproducibility and antibody accessibility. The new TIMP-1 assay significantly separates cancer and non-cancer and may as such be used for future clinical investigations of TIMP-1 as a new potential screening marker in CRC.

0-70 Lung

Pro-Gastrin-Releasing Peptide (ProGRP) in patients with lung pathologies: Comparison with CEA, CA 125, SCC, CYFRA 21-1 and NSE.

R. Molina, JM. Auge, X. Filella, N. Viñolas, J. Domingo-Domenech, R. Marrades.
Laboratory of Biochemistry (Oncobiology Unit). Oncology Unit, Hospital Clinic, IDIBAPS, Medical School, Barcelona, Spain.

Aims: In this study we compared the specificity and sensitivity of ProGRP with other tumor markers used in lung cancer (CEA, SCC, CYFRA and NSE)
Methods:87 patients with suspicious not confirmed lung cancer and 422 patients with lung cancer: 289 NSCLC and 133 small cell lung cancer (SCLC) were evaluated.
Results: Abnormal serum tumor marker specificity was higher than 93% with all tumor markers excluding CA 125 (75, 9%). CA 125 specificity increased to 89% when patients with effusions were excluded. Tumor marker sensitivities were CYFRA (>3.3 ng/ml) 61,4%, CEA (> 5ng/ml) 53%, CA 125 (>60 U/ml) 50.2%, SCC (> 2 ng/ml) 23,5%, NSE (>25 ng/ml) 11%, ProGRP (>40pg/ml) 24% in NSCLC and CYFRA 42%, CEA 50%, CA 125 39%, SCC 0%, NSE 53% and ProGRP 53% in SCLC. Tumor markers were related to the histological type and tumor extension. CEA highest concentrations were found in Adenocarcinomas, higher than in other groups of NSCLC or SCLC, SCC-highest in Squamous , ProGRP and NSE in SCLC compared to NSCLC. CYFRA was no related to the histological type. Likewise using the combination of 2 o 3 tumor markers it is possible to obtain a high sensitivity in all histologies: CEA, CYFRA 87% in Adenocarcinomas, CYFRA, SCC and CEA: 93% in Squamous tumors, ProGRP and NSE 81% in SCLC. In summary, ProGRP is the most sensitive marker in SCLC and CYFRA- in NSCLC.
Conclusions: Using a combination of tumor markers it is possible to suggest with high probability the histological type of lung cancer.

0-71 Lung

Differential diagnosis of lung tumors using the oncological biomarkers CEA, CYFRA 21-1, NSE and ProGRP: a multivariate analysis

C. Gruber, Stieber P, Hatz R [1], Holdenrieder S, Nagel D, Seidel D
Institute of Clinical Chemistry, Department of Surgery [1], Klinikum Grosshadern, University of Munich, Germany

Aims: This retrospective study was designed to verify the single and combined diagnostic value of CEA (AxSYM/Abbott), CYFRA 21-1 (ElecSys/Roche), NSE (Kryptor/Brahms) and ProGRP (ELISA/ALSI/IBL) in lung tumors.

Methods: The study included 1747 patients: 1325 suffered from primary lung cancer (LC), hereof 1015 from non small cell lung cancer (NSCLC) and 194 from small cell lung cancer (SCLC), 318 from benign lung diseases and 104 from lung metastases due to another primary.

Results: After univariate analysis of all markers for the differentiation between benign and malignant lung diseases, patients with extreme high values for at least one of the markers could be classified as malignant and thus be excluded from the further multivariate analysis.

A logistic regression model including age in addition to CEA, CYFRA 21-1 and NSE (used as logarithmic functions) was performed and from the coefficients of the model a score was calculated. ROC curves for this score and the single markers were evaluated.

The area under the curve (AUC) of the score of the combination of the three markers CYFRA 21-1, CEA, NSE and age was superior (AUC=0,84) to the AUC of the single markers: CYFRA 21-1 (AUC =0,79), CEA (AUC=0,72), NSE (AUC=0,59), ProGRP (AUC=0,57).

In the same way the capacity of the markers for histological classification of NSCLC and SCLC was investigated. In this model, CYFRA 21-1, NSE and ProGRP were included. The score also reached the best AUC (0,84), compared with NSE (AUC=0,81) and ProGRP (AUC=0,76).

Conclusions:, in cases of lung tumors of unknown origin the combined use of CEA, CYFRA 21-1, NSE and ProGRP is useful.

0-72 Lung

MUCINS (CA 125, CA 19.9, CA 15.3 AND TAG-72) AS TUMOR MARKERS IN PATIENTS WITH LUNG CANCER: COMPARISON WITH CYFRA 21-1, CEA, SCC AND NSE.

R. Molina, J. M. Augé, R. Marrades, N. Viñolas, Xavier Filella.
Oncobiology Unit, Oncology Department, Hospital Clinic, Medical School, Barcelona, Spain.

Aims: Tumor marker serum levels were prospectively studied in 214 with suspicious non confirmed lung cancer and in 348 patients with lung cancer (268 NSCLC patients, 80 SCLC patients). Abnormal serum levels (excluding renal failure and liver diseases) were found in: CEA 5%, CA 19.9 5,7%, CA 125 28%, NSE 1,4%,CYFRA 5%, TAG 6%, SCC 4% and CA 15.3 5%.

Methods: Tumor marker sensitivity was related to cancer histology and tumor extension.

Results: NSE was the tumor marker with the highest sensitivity in SCLC 84% and the lowest sensitivity in NSCLC (11%). Significantly higher concentrations of SCC (p=0,004, CA 15.3 (p= 0,001) and TAG (p=0,01) were found in NSCLC as opposed to SCLC. Likewise significantly higher levels of CEA (0,002), TAG (p=0,01), CA 15.3 (p= 0,006) were found in adenocarcinomas than in Squamous tumors. CA 19,9 were related to the histological type with the highest concentrations in adenocarcinomas, secondly in SCLC and the lowest in Squamous. In contrast, TAG and CA 15.3 were mainly found in adenocarcinomas, secondly in Squamous and the lowest in SCLC. The combination of 2 o 3 tumor markers show a high sensitivity in Mo (88-93%) and M1 (92-98%) lung cancer patients. Using tumor markers enables to suggest the histological diagnosis in 82% of the patients with an efficacy of 85%.

Conclusions: In summary, tumor markers are useful tools in the selection of high risk patients of lung cancer, in disease monitoring as well as in the aid of histological diagnosis.

0-73 Lung

Abstract not submitted.

0-74 Lung

Multiparametric analysis of prognosis in patients with advanced non-small cell lung cancer

Holdenrieder Stefan[1], von Pawel J[2], Raith H[2], Feldmann K[2], Stenman UH[3], Nagel D[1], Stieber P[1]
[1]University Hospital Munich-Grosshadern, Munich, Germany;
[2]Asklepios Hospital, Gauting, Germany;
[3]Helsinki University Central Hospital, Helsinki, Finland

Background: Currently available data concerning the prognostic relevance of biochemical markers in NSCLC are conflicting.
Methods: In a prospective study on 300 patients with newly diagnosed, advanced NSCLC undergoing chemotherapy, we investigated 60 pretherapeutic parameters including 23 clinical factors, 22 "classical" laboratory markers, and 15 oncological biomarkers. First, clinical parameters with independent prognostic relevance were selected by Cox-regression analysis. Second, all log-transformed values of biochemical markers and relevant clinical factors were included in Cox-regression analyses with backward selection using 100 bootstrap replications of the data set. Finally, all markers which remained in the model >25% of the runs were analyzed by Cox-regression using both forward and backward selection in parallel.
Results: Median survival of 172 deceased patients was 6.3 months; median observation time of 128 censored patients was 7.3 months. Of clinical factors, performance score (PS), weight loss (WL), metastases other than lung (MOL), and mode of therapy showed prognostic relevance. In bootstrap analyses, 22 markers were retained >25% of the runs in the model. The final multivariate model comprised PS, MOL, ln-CRP, ln-CYFRA 21-1, ln-NSE, ln-CA72-4, and ln-hCGβ.
Conclusion: Standardized procedure for establishing prognosis in advanced NSCLC revealed PS, MOL, CRP, CYFRA 21-1, NSE, CA72-4, and hCGβ as independent prognostic markers.

0-75 Lung

Clinical Evaluation of Soluble Mesothelin-related Peptide (Mesomark) in Mesothelioma, Benign and Malignant Lung Diseases

Petra Stieber[1], Rudolph Hatz[2], Stefan Holdenrieder[1], Judith Reinmiedl[4], Karin Hofmann[1], Andreas Schalhorn[3], [1]Institute of Clinical Chemistry, [2]Department of Surgery, [3]Internal Medicine III, University Hospital Munich-Grosshadern, Munich, Germany; [4]Asklepios Hospital, Gauting, Germany

Background: Soluble mesothelin-related peptide – a 40kDa protein which is expressed and released by mesothelioma cells and detected by the antibodies OV569 and 4H3 – is supposed to be a promising marker for mesothelioma detection in blood.
Methods: We investigated soluble mesothelin-related peptide in the sera of 148 healthy individuals, 26 patients with mesothelioma, 106 patients with various benign lung diseases and 428 patients with malignant lung diseases (among them 195 squamous, 119 adeno, 59 large-cell, and 45 small-cell lung cancer) using the Mesomark-ELISA (Fujirebio, USA; Schering, Germany).
Results: Median mesothelin related peptide concentrations were lowest in healthy individuals (1.0 nM; range 0.3-6.1 nM), followed by benign lung diseases (1.2 nM; 0.4-8.0 nM), lung cancer (1.4 nM; 0.2-12.7 nM) and mesothelioma (2.0 nM; 0.8-27.2 nM). The 95th percentiles were comparable for benign lung diseases and lung cancers (3.4 nM) except mesothelioma but significantly superior for mesothelioma patients (24.4 nM). At 95%-specificity for healthy individuals (1.9 nM), sensitivities for benign lung diseases, lung cancer and mesothelioma were 25%, 25%, and 50%, respectively; at 95%-specificity for benign lung diseases (3.4 nM), sensitivities for lung cancer and mesothelioma were 4% and 26%, respectively.
Conclusion: First clinical data confirm the high specificity of soluble mesothelin-related peptide for mesothelioma in high concentrations. Further investigations including other cancers and relevant benign diseases are ongoing to show the diagnostic value of this promising marker.

0-76 Lung

Autoantibodies in Lung Cancer.

Caroline Chapman[1], A. Murray[2], J. McElveen[2], U. Sahin[3], U. Luxemburger[3], O.Tureci[3], R. Wiewrodt[3], A. Barnes[2], J. Robertson[1].Division of Breast Surgery, Nottingham City Hospital, Nottingham, UK[1] OncImmune Ltd, BioCity, Nottingham, UK[2].Mainz "Johannes Gutenberg" University, Germany[2]

Aims: To demonstrate the diagnostic potential afforded by the detection of multiple autoantibodies to tumour-associated antigens in lung cancer.
Lung cancer is the worlds' leading cause of cancer deaths. Of the two main types of lung cancer (non–small cell lung cancer -NSCLC and small cell lung cancer - SCLC) NSCLC is generally less aggressive and more likely to be found before it has spread. However, lung cancers of all types are frequently not found until the cancer has advanced. Immune responses to a number of tumour-associated antigens have been reported, although their suitability, individually, as diagnostic indicators has not been demonstrated.
Methods: Autoantibodies to p53, HER2, NY-ESO, GBU4-5 and CAGE were measured in plasma, by ELISA in: normal controls (n=50); NSCLC (n=58) and SCLC (n=11).
Results: Elevated levels of autoantibodies were seen in 68% of lung cancer patients (71% NSCLC and 46% SCLC) with a specificity of 90%. Positivity of individual antigens ranged from 28% to 40%. No significant difference was seen in overall detection when these patients were subdivides by tumour grade or subtype.
Conclusions: This study raises the possibility of using a combination of assays to detect autoantibodies to cancer-associated antigens for screening and early diagnosis of lung cancer.

0-77 Melanoma

S100 proteins as cancer biomarkers with focus on S100B – biochemical properties, genomic organization and biological functions

Roland Einarsson, CanAg Diagnostics AB, Gothenburg, Sweden

The S100 protein family belongs to the S100/calmodulin/ troponin C superfamily. This group of proteins has grown from originally two members, S100A1 and S100B, to one of the largest subfamilies of EF-hand Ca^{2+}-binding proteins. Today 20 members of S100 proteins, a multigenic family of low molecular weight proteins (10-12 kDa), have been identified. The S100 proteins demonstrate a divers pattern of cell- and tissue-specific distribution, subcellular expression and intra- and extracellular functions. These functions are brought through interaction with different target proteins and posttranslational modifications. The structural organization of S100 genes is highly conserved. Sixteen S100 genes have been found to be clustered on human chromosome 1q21. In contrast to S100A proteins, S100B is located on chromosome 21q22).

A wide range of diseases, including neurologic diseases, chronic inflammation, and cancer have been linked to deregulation of S100 gene expression. Therefore, S100 proteins are considered for their potential use in clinical diagnostics as well as for therapy.

Protein S100B is an acidic protein. The isomers S100B and S100A1 form either homodimers (S100BB) or heterodimers (S100A1B). S100B is mainly found in astrocytes/glial cells in the brain and melanocytes. S100B binds 4 Ca^{2+}/dimer, most of which can be displaced by Zn^{2+} indicating a large variability of different structures. Its value in the immunohistochemical diagnosis of tumors of melanocytic origin is well established. Elevated blood levels of S100B protein have been demonstrated in melanoma showing its potential value in establishing prognosis, monitoring treatment and prediction of metastatic disease.

0-78 Melanoma

New Markers for Metastatic Uveal Melanoma

J. Pe'er,[1] R. Folberg,[3] K. S. Frenkel,[1] I. Kalickman,[2] Vivian Barak,[2]
[1]Department of Opthalmology, and [2]Immunology Laboratory for Tumor Diagnosis, Hadassah-Hebrew University Medical Center, Jerusalem Israel; [3]Department of Pathology, University of Illinois at Chicago, Chicago, Illinois

Aims: To test Osteopontin, S-100 and MIA as potential markers for metastatic uveal melanoma.
Methods: We have assessed over 1000 blood samples of uveal melanoma patients. (pts) We evaluated 15 pts with proven metastatic uveal melanoma, 67 pts under follow-up for more than 10 years without metastatic disease. For the 15 pts with metastases, we had kinetics before and after diagnosis of metastases. In addition, 50 healthy age-and sex-matched controls were included. All 3 markers were evaluated by ELISA assays. Tissue sections of metastatic melanoma were stained for Osteopontin and its RNA measured by RT PCR.
Results: Serum levels of Osteopontin in pts with metastases were almost 3 times higher (28± 2.6) than in NED (9.44± 1.8) pts with long follow-up and the control group (6.71± 1.2) ($p<0.001$). There was a significant rise in Osteopontin levels in the 15 pts who developed metastases during the study and corresponded to liver metastasis. The levels of S-100 in pts with metastases were three times higher (0.147± 0.04) than those of pts with long follow-up (0.057±0.01) and the control group(0.073±0.03), but there was no statistical significance. (0.07) There was no significant difference in MIA levels among the 3 groups: metastatic pts.-7.45±0.67, NED pts.-5.99±0.46 and controls 6.3± 0.26. By RT PCR highly invasive primary and metastatic uveal melanoma expressed 6 to 250 fold excess Osteopontin RNA compared to poorly invasive uveal melanoma cells.
Conclusions: Osteopontin and S-100 serum levels can serve as markers of metastatic disease of uveal melanoma. Increasing levels of both markers are prognostic of metastatic disease development.

0-79 Melanoma

Clinical utility of serum S100 and MIA in the Therapy Monitoring of patients with High Risk Malignant Melanoma.

Josep Maria Auge (1), R Molina (1), J Domingo (2), S Puig (3), X Filella (1), J Malvehy (3), T Castel 3), AM Ballesta (1). (1) Biochemistry (2) Medical Oncology (3) Dermatology Departments. Hospital Clinic, IDIBAPS, Barcelona, Spain.

Aims: To study the clinical utility of S100 and MIA in the therapy monitoring and early diagnosis of recurrence of high-risk melanoma surgically treated and under high doses of adjuvant Interferon alfa2b.
Patients and Methods: S100 (n=97) and MIA (n=50) were studied pre-treatment, after 3 months and at the end of treatment (12 months) or at the diagnosis of recurrence.
Results: Abnormal S100 (>0,15µg/L) and MIA (>12ng/mL) at 3 months of initiating the adjuvant treatment, were found in 1,9% and 0% of patients without recurrence and in 41,9% and 12,0% of patients with recurrence, respectively. Comparing tumor marker concentrations at the beginning of treatment and after 3 months, significantly higher S100 levels (p<0,01) and MIA (p=0,03) were found in those patients that didn't respond and presented relapse during follow-up. At progression, 62,8% and 36,4% of patients with recurrence showed abnormal S100 and MIA levels, respectively. Using a dynamic criteria of 25% change for S100, between pre-treatment levels and after 3 months, we observed that 71% of non responding patients showed increasing levels. In contrast, 68,8% of patients without recurrence, showed decreasing or no changes in the S100 levels (p<0,01). S100>0,15µg/L after 3 months and an increasing pattern were found as an independent prognostic factor, with shorter DFS and OS.
Conclusions: S100 is useful to discriminate between responders and nonresponders to immunotherapy as well as to determine early diagnosis of recurrence. The inclusion of MIA does not increase significantly the S100 results.

0-80 Melanoma

Xenogeneic cells as anticancer vaccine

Severin Sergey
Moscow Research Institute of Medical Ecology, JSC "Russian Biotechnologies"

Aims: Elaboration of the method enabling cultivation of xenogeneic cells in live organism for stimulation of specific anti-tumor immunity Beeing injected under the skin, inert polyacrylamide gel routinely used in plastic surgery forms a capsule of connective tissue. The formation of such a capsule promotes the growth of xenogenic tumor cells eventually resulting in the development of a solid tumor. Subsequent rejection of the tumor elicits specific immunity to antigenically similar syngeneic tumors.
Methods: Model experiments were carried out on 57Black/6 mice with syngeneic melanoma -16 and xenogeneic human melanoma SK-Mel-1. For clinical trials on patients with melanoma xenogeneic mouse melanoma B-16 has been used. Polyacrylamide gel was injected s/c 1–2 months prior to injection of tumor cells.
Results: Animal studies revealed a protective effect of human melanoma cells against cells of transplanted murine tumor. Complete safety of murine melanoma -16 for human beings was demonstrated on human volunteers and patients with melanoma in the first stage of clinical trials.
Current second stage of clinical trials is confirming a pronounced stimulation of specific immunity against human melanoma
Conclusions: Live xenogenic neoplastic cells constituting a solid tumor formed inside a connective tissue capsule can serve as a basis for the design of prophylactic and therapeutic vaccines.

0-81 Melanoma

Xenovaccination of patients with skin melanoma: phase I/II clinical trial

Vladimir Moiseyenko, I.Baldueva, A.Danilov, A.Danilova
Russian Biotechnologies, Moscow, Russia

It is reported that xenovaccination of BDF$_1$ and $_{57}$ 1$_6$ mice with reinoculated human melanoma (SK.MEL-28) cells or with primary cell cultures of human melanoma encapsulated into polyacrylamide gel (PAAG) results in a biologically significant (>70%) inhibition of growth of the syngeneic melanoma -16 and the appearance of activated cytotoxic lymphocytes.
Aims: To assess clinical and immunological efficiency of PAAG xenovaccination in patients with high risk skin melanoma.
Methods: After signing an informed consent 30 patients with histologically verified skin melanoma grades IV-V invasion (according to Clarke) that underwent radical operations were enrolled in the study. The tested material included PAAG and cell cultures of murine melanoma -16.
Results: Stimulation of immune response was noticed on the 14th and 30th post-vaccination days and was manifested in increased populations of CD3$^+$, CD4$^+$ and CD8$^+$ -lymphocytes (P=.02, P=.03 and P=.05, respectively).The activation peak of CD4$^+$ cells on the day 14(P=.02), of CTL CD8$^+$ cells on the day 30(P=.05) and the DTH response in 81% of patients testify to the indisputably high immunogenicity of the vaccine.A specific response of T cells against human melanoma cells expressing melanoma-associated antigens (tyrosinase, Mel A, CD63, MAGE1, S100, gp100) and HLA Class I, II was observed in 16% of vaccinated patients (ELISPOT IFN and granzyme B).
Conclusions: Xenovaccination is associated with DTH and stimulates a specific antigen immune response during the early follow-up period.

0-82 Urology

Cell-free DNA and RNA in plasma as a new molecular marker for prostate cancer.

Papadopoulou E, Davilas E, Sotiriou V, Koliopanos A, Aggelakis F, Dardoufas K, Agnanti N, Karydas I, Nasioulas G.

Molecular Biology Research Center HYGEIA, Antonis Papayannis, Kiffisias Ave. & 4 Erythrou Stavrou Str., 151 23 Marousi, Athens, Hellas.

Extracellular nucleic acids could serve as molecular markers in the early detection of cancer and in the prediction of disease outcome. In this study we examined six molecular markers, such as: variations in the quantity of DNA in plasma, glutathione-S-transferase P1 (GSTP1) gene methylation status in plasma, carcinoembryonic antigen (CEA) and prostate-specific membrane antigen (PSMA) mRNA in peripheral blood mononuclear cells (PBMC), and plasma samples from prostate cancer patients in different stages. The combination of DNA load and GSTP1 promoter methylation status identified 83% (10/12) of the prostate cancer patients before therapy.
This study shows that free circulating DNA can be detected in patients with prostate cancer compared with disease-free individuals, and suggests anew, noninvasive approach for early detection of prostate cancer.

0-83 Urology

The use of PSA for screening of prostate cancer

Ulf-Håkan Stenman
Department of Clinical Chemistry, Helsinki University Central Hospital, FIN-00014 Helsinki University, Finland

Prostate cancer is now the most common cancer in men in industrialized countries while mortality is second only to lung cancer. It is thus a serious health problem. When detected clinically, prostate cancer is mostly incurable but men at risk can identified by screening based on determination of PSA in serum. Randomized studies initiated ten years ago will clarify whether screening will reduce mortality but results can be expected only after 5-10 more years. Recent results show that most screen-detected tumors are clinically localized and of intermediate grade, which has improved the chances of cure. In spite of this, about one third of patients treated radically when the tumor is clinically localized experience a relapse. However, according to some estimates 50-80% of the screen-detected tumors would not have developed into clinical disease during the lifetime of the patient. There is therefore a need to improve the screening strategies. Recent results show that the proportion of free PSA (%fPSA) predicts the risk of developing clinical disease already when serum PSA is below the presently used cutoff values of 2.5 – 4 ng/ml. By starting screening at a younger age and monitoring the change in PSA and %fPSA it will be possible to find cancers that need to be cured at an earlier stage while avoiding detection of indolent tumors that do not threaten the health and life of the patient.

0-84 Urology

Abstract not submitted.

0-85 Urology

NMP22-BladderChek in early bladder cancer detection

Oehr Peter
University Bonn, Germany

Aims: The new Matritech NMP22 BladderChek point of care (POC) assay was investigated compared to cytology, cystoscopy and histology.
Methods: The assay was used at practitioners' sites. Patients with urocystitis, stones, urinary tract infections and incorporated catheters were excluded.
Results: In case of NMP22 BladderChek, the sensitivity, specificity, positive predictive (PPV) and negative predictive (NPV) values in the hematuria group (N=212) were 82%, 98%, 82%, 98%, and in the follow-up group (N=206) 61%, 98%, 85%, and 94% respectively. Cystoscopy was false negative twice, and false positive twice.
Diagnostics by both NMP22 BladderChek and cytology were made in 252 cases (hematuria and follow-up). In only 4 cases (1.6%) both markers were false negative. When both markers were positive, the final result was true positive in every case. In the subgroup of hematuria patients (14 with tumor and 99 tumor-free), NMP22 BladderChek had 86% sensitivity and 98% specificity compared to cytology with 57% and 97%, respectively. There were no tumor-free patients for whom both tests were false positive.
Conclusions: Cytology in addition to NMP22 BladderChek can improve specificity in hematuria patients. No incidences in which both were false positive in the 99 true negative cases is like a 100% exclusion criterion. When both markers are positive in a patient, the result appears to be a 100% inclusion criterion for cancer. The fact that cystoscopy was false in 4 out of 418 cases demonstrates the need for an accurate adjunctive test.

0-86 Urology

Reference Range Values For Free/Total PSA May Vary Clinically Significant Between Assay Systems

Axel Semjonow 1, M. Füchtenkötter 1, M. Kranz 1, F. Oberpenning 2, E. Eltze 3, O.Bettendorf 3, G. Angelis 4
1-Prostate Center, Dept. of Urology, Univ. Münster; 2-Dept. of Urology, Univ. Bonn 3-Prostate Center, Institute of Pathology and 4-Dept. of Clin. Chemistry, Univ. Münster, Germany

Aims: To compare reference ranges of two assay systems for free (F) and total (T) PSA in a population of men prior to systematic trans-rectal ultrasound-guided prostate biopsy (Bx).
Methods: Serum samples of 617 men drawn before Bx were used to determine F- and T-PSA prospectively with two assay systems, Beckman-Coulter Hybritech Access (A) and Vidas, BioMerieux (V). The results of Bx were used to validate the reference ranges of the assays A and V. T-PSA concen-trations of all men ranged between 2 and 20 ng/ml as measured with assay V.
Results: 334 men had benign biopsies and 283 had prostate cancer (PCa). The areas under receiver operating characteristics curves (AUC) for T-PSA were 0.53 (95% CI: 0.49-0.57) and 0.54 (95% CI: 0.50-0.58) for Assay A and V, respectively (p = n.s.). In both assay systems F/T-PSA was superior to T-PSA. The AUC for F/T-PSA were 0.66 and 0.71 ($p<0.001$) for assay A and V, respectively. The median F/T-PSA in pts. with benign Bx vs. PCa was 15% vs. 11% in assay A and 20% vs. 13% in assay V.
Conclusions: The capability of assay sys-tems measuring F/T-PSA to differentiate between benign Bx and PCa may differ statistically significant. To achieve best results, the reference range applied, needs to be assay-specific. Using "traditional" reference ranges may result in unnecessary Bx or overlooked PCa and may thus reduce diagnostic accuracy.

0-87 Urology

Defining molecular profiles of poor outcome in patients with invasive bladder cancer using oligonucleotide microarrays

Sanchez-Carbayo Marta, Socci Nicholas, Lozano Juanjo, Saint Fabien, Cordon-Cardo Carlos. Memorial Sloan-Kettering Cancer Center, New York, USA.

Aims: to define genetic signatures characteristic of aggressive clinical behavior in advanced bladder tumors.
Methods: Transcript profiles of 157 bladder tissues were analyzed using oligonucleotide arrays. Hierarchical clustering and supervised algorithms were used to stratify bladder tumors based on their stage, node metastases and survival. IHC analyses on bladder tissue arrays (n=294 cases) served to validate associations between marker expression, staging and outcome.
Results: Hierarchical clustering classified normal urothelium, superficial and invasive tumors with 82.2% accuracy and stratified bladder tumors based on clinical outcome. Predictive algorithms rendered 89% correct rate for tumor staging. Accuracies of 82% and 90% were obtained for predicting overall survival when considering all patients with bladder cancer, or only patients with invasive disease, respectively. A genetic profile consisting of 174 probes was identified in those patients with positive lymph nodes and poor survival. Two independent global test runs concluded the robust association or this profile with lymph node metastases (p= 7.3e-13), and overall survival (p= 1.9e-14) simultaneously. IHCl analyses on tissue arrays sustained the significant association of synuclein with tumor staging and clinical outcome (p=0.002).
Conclusions: Gene profiling provides a classification scheme of diagnostic and prognostic utility for stratifying advanced bladder cancer. Identification of this poor outcome profile could assist in selecting patients who may benefit from more aggressive therapeutic intervention.

0-88 Urology

Modulation of telomerase expression by indols and estrogens in Prostate Cancer cells

Adler S., Zemer R., Klein A.

Molecular Biology Lab, Meir Hospital, Tel-Aviv University, Kfar Saba, Israel

Aims: Activation of telomerase is an essential step in cancer cells immortalization and cancer progression. Modulation of its expression may be beneficial for controlling cancer cell proliferation. Prostate cancer patients are treated with estrogens in order to abolish testicular androgens. Studies with the phytochemical Indole-3-Carbinol (I3C) showed its anti-proliferation capabilities. Aims: In the present study we examined the effect of the synthetic estrogen- Diethylstilbest (DES) and I3C on transcription and activation of telomerase in PC3 human prostate cell line.
Methods: Transcription was analysed by real time RT-PCR techniques and telomerase activity was measured by semiquantitative TRAP method.
Results: I3C, at concentrations of 100 and 250 μM, showed trancription inhibition rates of 18 and 25 % respectively, whereas DES, at concentrations of 10 and 50•μM, showed enhancement rates of 115 and 470% respectively. However activation of telomerase was found to be inhibited by both compounds: I3C 100 μM 28%; I3C 250•μM - 47%, DES 10•μM - 14%; DES50•μM - 54%. An almost complete inhibition was obtained in the presence of both compounds. I3C and DES did not affect the activation of telomerase in In Vitro studies.
Conclusions: The results of this study imply that the combination of I3C with DES may have a beneficial effect on proliferation arrest of prostate cancer cells.

0-89 Urology

Pilot Study of Capillary Electrophoresis Coupled to Mass Spectrometry as a Tool to Define Potential Prostate Cancer Biomarkers in Urine

D. Theodorescu 1,D. Fliser 2, S. Wittke 3, H. Mischak 2, 3, R. Krebs 3, M. Walden 3 E. Eltze 4, O. Bettendorf 4, C. Wülfing 5, and Axel Semjonow 5
1 Paul Mellon Prostate Cancer Institute, University of Virginia, Charlottesville, USA; 2 Medical School Hannover, 3 Mosaiques Diagnostics & Therapeutics, Hannover; 4 University of Münster, Institute of Pathology; 5 Prostate Center, Dept. of Urology, Münster, Germany

Aims: We describe the use of capillary electrophoresis (CE) coupled with mass spectrometry (MS) to identify single polypeptides and patterns of polypeptides specific for prostate cancer in spontaneously voided initial human urine samples without prior prostate massage.
Methods: Using improved sample preparation methods that enable enhanced comparability between different samples, we examined samples from 47 patients that underwent prostate biopsy.
Results: 21 patients had benign pathology and 26 prostate cancer (CaP) and were used to define potential biomarkers which allow discrimination between these two conditions. In addition, CE-MS data from these 47 urine samples were compared to 41 young men (control) without known or suspected clinical CaP to further confirm the polypeptides indicative for CaP. Several polypeptides were selected that enabled correct classification of the CaP patients with 92% sensitivity and 96% specificity upon crossvalidation. We then examined additional 474 samples from patients with renal disease enrolled in other studies and found 14 (2.9%) which had polypeptides indicative for CaP possibly indicating that they harboured CaP, which will be further investigated.
Conclusions: This early pilot study suggests that CE-MS of urine warrants further investigation as a tool that can identify putative biomarkers for CaP.

0-90 Urology

Expression of transketolase TKTL1 predicts colon and urothelial cancer patient survival

Langbein Sigrun (1), Zerilli M. (2), Zur Hausen A. (3), Popa J. (1), Steidler A. (1), Alken P. (1), Stassi G. (2), Schubert P. (4), Coy J. F. (4)
(1) Dept. of Urology, University Hospital Mannheim, (2) Dept. of Surgical and Oncological Sciences, University of Palermo, (3) Dept. of Pathology, University of Freiburg, (4) R-Biopharm AG, Darmstadt

Aims: Malignant tumors ferment glucose to lactate even in the presence of oxygen (Warburg effect). The pentose phosphate pathway allows glucose conversion to ribose for DNA/RNA synthesis and glucose degradation to lactate. The nonoxidative part of the PPP is controlled by transketolase enzyme reactions. TKTL1 encodes a transketolase with unusual enzymatic properties. Here we examined the expression of the TKTL1 protein in colon and urothelial carcinomas, as well as its correlation with histopathological data and its possible impact on patients survival.
Methods: We performed a retrospective immunohistochemical study on paraffin embedded tissue microarrays of 70 colon carcinomas and 64 urothelial carcinomas using a TKTL1 specific monoclonal antibody.
Results: In colon as well as urothelial carcinomas the expression of TKTL1 correlated with invasiveness of tumors and patient survival.
Conclusions: The expression of TKTL1 transketolase predicts colon and urothelial patient survival. Besides this prognostic value, TKTL1 represents a novel pharmacodiagnostic marker, since inhibition of transketolase enzyme reactions suppresses tumour growth and metastasis. We propose an individualized and targeted cancer therapy, which is based on the determination and inhibition of TKTL1 in tumors.

0-91 Urology

Performance of Complexed versus Total Prostate Specific Antigen as first-line tests using Discordance Analysis Characteristics (DAC)

Frank Oberpenning [1], O. Bettendorf [2], G. D. Angelis [3], T. Keller [4], A. Semjonow [5]
[1] Dept. of Urology, Univ. of Bonn; [2] Prostate Center, Inst. of Pathology, [3] Dept. of Clin. Chemistry, Univ. Münster,[4] ACOMED Statistik, Leipzig, [5] Prostate Center, Dept. of Urology, Univ. Münster; Germany

Aims: Previous analyses of C-PSA versus T-PSA as first-line tests for early diagnosis of prostate cancer (PCA) rendered discrepancies, partly due to conflicting results from ROC-curve comparisons, where some bias results from the determination of PSA-ranges and cutoffs investigated. To overcome this bias, the method of DAC has recently been proposed. DAC focusses on analyzing individuals, who are discordantly categorized by 2 tests investigated for iterated cutoffs with identical sensitivity.
Methods: In sera from 401 men (T-PSA range 2-30 ng/ml), T- and F-PSA (Access) as well as C-PSA (Bayer) where determined prior to prostate biopsy and results related to biopsy outcome using DAC-analysis.
Results: Histology yielded 199 PCA and 202 men without PCA (nPCA). In clinically relevant ranges, DAC showed among discordantly tested patients, that C-PSA detected men with PCA with an over 3-fold better specificity than T-PSA. At >90%/>26% sensitivities a T-PSA range of 4.1 to 10 (n=255) corresponded to a C-PSA range of 2.9-7.2 (n= 262). Whithin these grey zones a 0.20 F/T-PSA matched with a 0.33 F/C-PSA at >90% sensitivity. Applying grey-zone triggered 2-step diagnostics (T-PSA & F/T-PSA vs. C-PSA & F/C-PSA) the first-line use of C -PSA triggered 7 additional F-PSA-determinations, however it detected 2 additional cancers while saving 7 unnecessary biopsies.
Conclusions: C-PSA seems moderately superior to T-PSA as a first-line test in prostate cancer diagnostics. The DAC method gives additional information to ROC analyses of subgroups when evaluating 2 markers.

0-92 Urology

Detailed analysis of histopathological parameters and PCA3 test results

van Gils Martijn, Hessels D, Hulsbergen - van de Kaa C, Witjes F, Mulders P, Schalken J
Department of Urology, Radboud University Nijmegen Medical Centre, The Netherlands

Aims: PCA3 gene expression is prostate specific and is strongly up-regulated in prostate cancer cells compared to non-malignant prostate cells. We have successfully demonstrated that PCA3 gene based analysis can detect prostate cancer cells in urinary sediments after extended DRE. Consequently PCA3 has potential in prostate cancer diagnosis. Based on the hypothesis that more aggressive tumours could grow in a more invasive manner and shed more cancer cells in the prostatic ducts, just recently we have also demonstrated that PCA3 gene based analysis has potential as a prognostic parameter. Therefore, we correlated the results of PCA3 gene based analysis in urinary sediments to the histopathological parameters of the radical prostatectomy specimens in the same prostate cancer patients.
Methods: In our clinic a cohort of prostate cancer patients, to be treated by radical prostatectomy, received study information and signed informed consent in order to enter the study. We compared the histopathological parameters of the radical prostatectomy specimens to the ratio PCA3/PSA mRNA in urinary sediments obtained from the same 52 patients before surgery.
Results: No clear correlation was seen between the histological parameters and the levels of the PCA3/PSA mRNA ratios.
Conclusions: We conclude that the absence of a clear correlation between the histological parameters and the levels of the PCA3/PSA mRNA ratios is most likely caused by patient selection for surgical treatment.

0-93 Urology – GEN PROBE SYMPOSIUM

PCA3 gene based analysis of urinary sediments has prognostic value.

Hessels Daphne, van Gils M, Mulders P, Witjes F, Schalken J
Experimental Urology, Nijmegen Centre for Molecular Life Sciences, The Netherlands

Aims: The PCA3 gene is strongly over-expressed in prostate cancer when compared to non malignant prostate epithelial cells due to a unique mechanism of transcriptional regulation. We successfully demonstrated that cancer cells can be detected in urinary sediments after extended DRE and therefore PCA3 may have a potential diagnostic application. We hypothesized that aggressive cells are more invasive and thus are more likely to mobilize and shed into the ductal system. Therefore, the ratio PCA3/PSA mRNA was determined in urinary sediments after extended DRE and correlated with biological aggressiveness.
Methods: A new cohort of patients that entered our clinic with elevated serum levels (>3ng/ml) was tested prospectively. The patients received study information and signed informed consent in order to enter the study. For histological assessment ultrasound guided biopsy for the presence or absence of malignancy was performed. In 49 patients cancer was identified by histopathological evaluation of the biopsies. We compared the histology with the PCA3/PSA mRNA ratio obtained immediately before the biopsies.
Results: A clear correlation was seen between Gleason (sum) score and the level of PCA3/PSA mRNA ratios. The mean value of the PCA3/PSA ratio in case of Gleason 4 and 5 is 41, in case of Gleason 6 it is 163, in case of Gleason 7 it is 193 and in case of Gleason 8 it is 577. Subsequently, we analyzed distribution of Gleason grades in cases of which the test was positive/true positive and the ones in which the test was negative. The false negatives were of significant lower grade than the true positive.
Conclusions: We therefore conclude that the PCA3/PSA mRNA ratio analyzed in urinary sediments after extended DRE has potential as a prognostic parameter.

0-94 Urology – GEN PROBE SYMPOSIUM

Development and Performance of the APTIMA® PCA3 Molecular Urine Test for Prostate Cancer

Brentano Steven[1], Groskopf J[1], Walker S[1], Deras I[1], Clark C[1], Bodrug S[1], Blase A[1], Desaulniers M[2], Fradet Y[2], Marks L[3], Rittenhouse H[1]
[1]Gen-Probe Incorporated, San Diego, CA; [2]DiagnoCure Incorporated, Quebec, Canada; [3]Urological Sciences Research Foundation, Los Angeles, CA

Aims: PCA3 mRNA is prostate-specific and highly over-expressed in prostate tumor cells. We used the APTIMA PCA3 Transcription-Mediated Amplification (TMA) research assay to quantify PCA3 and PSA mRNAs derived from prostate cells in whole urine. Sensitivity and specificity were assessed in two different studies to investigate the assay's potential clinical utility as a diagnostic aid for prostate cancer.
Methods: 355 pre-biopsy and 62 pre-prostatectomy urine specimens were collected by DiagnoCure (DC) and 71 pre-biopsy samples at Urological Sciences Research Foundation (USRF). PCA3 and PSA mRNAs were isolated from post-DRE urine, amplified and quantified with prototype assays utilizing Gen-Probe target capture, TMA and chemiluminescent detection technologies. Biopsy results were correlated with the ratio of PCA3/PSA mRNAs. PSA copy level was used to normalize PCA3 signal and confirm sufficient PSA mRNA to yield an informative result.
Results: The DC population included 180 biopsy-positives and 237 biopsy-negatives (138 PIN and ASAP), and USRF included 15 biopsy-positives and 56 biopsy-negatives. Receiver operating characteristics (ROC) curves determined specificity and sensitivity compared to biopsy. Specificity, sensitivity and area under the ROC curve (AUC) for the DC population were 76%, 50% and 0.68; excluding PIN and ASAP increased AUC to 0.78. Specificity, sensitivity and AUC for the USRF population were 91%, 60% and 0.76. Overall specimen informative rate was 95.3%.

0-95 Abbott symposium: – New Aspects in the Clinical Utility of Tumor Markers

Squamous Cell Carcinoma Antigen (SCC) in Clinical Practice

R. Molina, JM. Augé, X. Filella Oncobiology Unit, Laboratory of Biochemistry, Hospital Clinic. Medical School, Barcelona, Spain. The Oncobiology Unit has been using routinely the SCC in the following protocols:

Lung Cancer. We are determining five tumor markers, SCC, CYFRA, CA 125, CEA and NSE at diagnosis, and in the follow-up of patients with cancer. CYFRA is the most sensitive marker in NSCLC and NSE in SCLC, but SCC is a key marker to distinguish the tumor histology. Abnormal SCC indicates NSCLC with a probability higher than 95%, mainly squamous tumors. Likewise SCC is an independent prognostic factor, and the serial determination is of high interest in the early diagnosis of recurrence as well as in disease monitoring. Squamous cervical cancer. Our protocol includes SCC as the tumor marker of choice in this malignancy as well as CYFRA and CEA as complementary tumor markers. In our experience, SCC sensitivity range from 26% in stage I until 83% in stage IV. The main clinical application is a help to diagnosis, staging and choice of treatment. SCC serum levels were clearly related to the tumor stage, parametrial invasion, tumor size and nodal involvement. Likewise, pretreatment SCC is an independent prognostic factor in univariate and multivariate analysis and the serial determination of this tumor marker is useful in the early diagnosis of recurrence and follow-up. In our experience, SCC was the first sign of recurrence in 67% of the 69 patients with recurrence diagnosed in the last five years. The inclusion of CYFRA and CEA improve the utility in early diagnosis being one or another tumor marker the first sign of recurrence in 94% of the patients. Head and Neck malignancy. SCC is the most sensitive tumor marker in this malignancy, sensitivity ranged from 18% in stage I to 60% in stage IV. This sensitivity is related to the histological type and site of the malignancy. Larynx tumors are those with the highest SCC sensitivity and piriform recess those with the lowest sensitivity. The main clinical applications are in prognosis and follow-up.

Unknown primary malignancy. We used a protocol trying to help to the clinician in the fast discrimination of patients with suspicious sign of cancer. Evaluation of 1834 patients clearly indicated that SCC is a key marker to distinguish, squamous tumors and discriminate the histology in those with suspicios lung, cervical or head and neck Ca.

0-96 Abbott symposium: – New Aspects in the Clinical Utility of Tumor Markers

Impact of different total and free PSA assays within ProstataClass based ANNs: Comparison in 798 Patients

Carsten Stephan1, Henning Cammann2, Hellmuth Meyer1, Moritz Klaas1, and Klaus Jung1, Department of 1Urology and 2Institute for Medical Biometry, University Hospital Charité, Schumannstrasse 20/21, D-10098 Berlin, Germany

Various studies have proven discordant concentrations of total and free prostate-specific antigen (tPSA, fPSA) obtained with different assays. These assay-dependent variations could result in misinterpretations of individual PSA values with possibly wrong clinical decisions to diagnose prostate carcinoma (PCa). The impact of thesevariations on artificial neural networks (ANNs) were estimated. We investigated archival sera collected between February 2001 and June 2004 from 798 untreated and histologically proven men (468 PCa and 330 BPH) with tPSA concentrations between 0.49 and 25 µg/L. We parallel measured tPSA and fPSA concentration with 5 different assays including the AxSYM System (Abbott Diagnostics). Different models of our ProstataClass ANN were compared. The AxSYM tPSA assays measured free and bound PSA equimolar which was not seen in most other assays. The median percent free PSA (%fPSA) values were highest for the Abbott assays for all BPH patients (22.2%, lowest: 14.2% with DPC) and PCa patients (12.5%, lowest: 8.1% with DPC) indicating already large differences especially in BPH patients (8%). ROC analysis showed always a significantly better performance of the classic ProstataClass program compared to %fPSA regardless of the assay used. However, new ANN models built with data from the respective assay further improve the outcome of the ANNs. Despite a relatively good performance of the ANN program ProstataClass there is seen a further improvement when ANN models were generated with data for each assay.

P-1 Urology

Diagnostic value of urinary bladder cancer (UBC) antigen for urinary bladder transitional cell carcinoma (TCC)

Marshutina N[1], Sergeeva N[1], Rodina I[1], Rusakov I[1], Sergeeva V[2]
Moscow Herzen Research On ological Institute[1], Moscow State Medical University[2], Russia

Aims: The purpose of the present work was to evaluate the clinical significance of new urinary antigen – UBC (cytokeratine fragments 8/18) for primary patients with TCC of urinary bladder.
Methods: UBC antigen levels in urine were analyzed by ELISA kit (IDL, Biotech, Sweden) and corrected according creatinine (CREA) level. UBC was measured in urine of 198 patients prior to therapy: gr I - 60 pts. with TCC of urinary bladder (25 – superficial bladder cancer (BC); 35 – invasive BC), gr II - 38 pts. with BC in remission; gr III - 12 pts. with renal carcinoma; gr IV - 21 pts. with nonurological cancers; gr V – 19 pts. with papilloma of bladder; gr VI - 48 pts. with non-malignant urological diseases; and - 18 healthy donors (gr VII).
Results: Mean UBC levels were (75,7±13,2; 1,9±0,3; 9,6±7,8; 1,8±0,4; 4,3±1,2; 2,7±1,0; 0,5±0,3)x10^{-4} mkg/mkmol CREA for groups I to VII, respectively. The UBC levels for superficial BC were lower than for invasive BC: (26.1±8.2 vs 111.1±20.2)x10^{-4} mkg/mkmol CREA. For discriminant UBC level 4,9x10^{-4} mkg/mkmol CREA, the sensitivity of UBC for TCC of urinary bladder was 86,7 %, specificity 86,4 %. The sensitivity of UBC for the detection of recurrent tumors was 80%. Enhanced antigen levels were found for 3 cases of renal pelvis cancer (gr III), 1 stomach cancer and 1 uterine cervical cancer (gr IV); 5 papilloma of bladder (gr V); 5 cystitis, 2 bladder polyps, 2 cases of urolitiasis (gr VI).
Conclusions: This study provides evidence, that UBC antigen has high sensitive diagnostic and prognostic properties with good specificity for TCC of urinary bladder. As noninvasive diagnostic test, UBC antigen is superior to routine cytology for primary diagnosis of urinary bladder TCC and for monitoring these patients.

P-2 Urology

Can ProPSA improve prostate cancer specificity within the Prostata Class artificial neural network?

Stephan Carsten, Cammann H, Kwiatkowski M, Jung K
Dept. of Urology & Institute for Medical Biometry, Charité Hospital Berlin, Germany and Dept. of Urology, Kantonsspital Aarau, Switzerland

Aims: ProPSA and artificial neural networks (ANNs) with PSA, %fPSA, age, prostate volume, and status of digital rectal examination (DRE) have been shown to improve specificity over percent free PSA (%fPSA) for prostate cancer (PCa) diagnosis. This study was performed to test the ability of proPSA within different ProstataClass ANNs.
Methods: ProPSA (Roche assay) were measured at the Charite Hospital Berlin in 898 patients taken from 2 centers. Comparison of parameters were performed with ROC analysis using the area under the curve (AUC) and specificities at 95% sensitivity. 12 Different ANNs with inclusion of the laboratory parameters: PSA, fPSA, pro PSA and proPSA ratios and additional clinical data like prostate volume and/or DRE were compared.
Results: ProPSA was only within the tPSA range 1-4 ng/ml significantly higher in the PCa patients (Aarau). Only at tPSA 4.1-10 ng/ml (Berlin) the AUC for proPSA/%fPSA (0.78) was larger than for %fPSA (0.75) and the ANN only with laboratory data (0.84) further improved outcome and was equal to the classical ProstataClass ANN (0.84). However, at 95% sensitivity only the ANN with all parameters reached significance to %fPSA (p=0.002).
Conclusions: The overall advantage of proPSA (Roche assay) is limited to subgroups only. But at tPSA 4.1-10 ng/ml the inclusion of proPSA into the ProstataClass ANN may avoid the need of prostate volume and DRE. The use of proPSA at the clinically important point of 95% sensitivity should be combined with additional clinical data and algorithms like ANNs to improve PCa specificity.

P-3 Urology

A possible correlation between ZIP2 messenger RNA expression and zinc level in rat lateral prostate

Iguchi Kazuhiro , Ito M, Usui S, Hirano K
Laboratory of Pharmaceutics, Gifu Pharmaceutical University, Mitahora-higashi, Gifu, Japan

Aims: Prostate gland contains a higher concentration of zinc than any other organ in the body, however, the zinc retention system in the prostate remains unclear. In prostate cancer, zinc contents are significantly lower than those in the surrounding normal prostate tissues, and the reduced zinc content in the prostate tumor cells has been shown to lead to increased cell growth, invasion, and decreased sensitivity to cytotoxic agents. Thus, the functions of zinc in the prostate gland have been revealed gradually, however, the mechanism of zinc accumulation in the prostate gland remains unknown. The elucidation of the zinc retention system in the prostate will be useful for investigating prostatic diseases. In the present study, we examined the expression of zinc transporters in rat prostate.
Methods: The mRNA expressions of zinc transporters (ZnT1, ZnT2, ZIP1, ZIP2) were determined by RT-PCR analysis and real-time quantitative RT-PCR analysis. Zinc was assayed by atomic absorption, after samples were treated with tricholoroacetic acid/nitric acid solution.
Results: We found that ZnT2 and ZIP2 mRNA were expressed at high level in rat lateral prostate (LP). The ZIP2 mRNA expression was decreased in castrated LP, associated with a decrease in zinc level, and these changes were reversed by testosterone replacement. Moreover, ZIP2 expression levels in LP positively correlated with the zinc levels. The expression of other zinc transporters (ZnT1, ZnT2, ZIP1) did not correlated with the zinc levels.
Conclusions: These findings suggest that ZIP2 is involved in zinc homeostasis of rat prostate.

P-4 Urology

P1NP serum concentration in prostate cancer patients in respect to bone scan findings

Rychlik Urszula, Kulpa JK, Tarapacz J, Zawiła K, Brandys K, Jaszczy ski J
Center of Oncology – M.Skłodowska-Curie Memorial Institute, Cracow Division, Poland

Aims: In prostate cancer, bones are a frequent locations of metastases. The method of choice for diagnosing bone metastasis is scintigraphy with high sensitivity, but low specificity. This stimulates the search for other methods which could give complementary information about occurrence of bone metastases. The aim of study was the assessment of P1NP and other bone markers in prostate cancer patients in relation to bone scan findings.
Methods: The determinations of P1NP, osteocalcin, •CTx, PSA and ALP were performed in a group of 100 not hormonally treated prostate cancer patients indicated for bone scintigraphy and in the reference group.
Results: No differences between prostate cancer patients without bone metastases and the reference group were found in P1NP, osteocalcin, •CTx and ALP, whereas PSA was significantly higher in the first group. In prostate cancer patients with bone metastases in comparison with the reference group, and also with patients free from metastases, significantly higher levels of PSA and bone markers were found. ROC analysis revealed that P1NP determinations exhibit the best utility for differentiation of prostate cancer patients for the presence of bone metastases. The sensitivity of P1NP at 95% specificity for the detection of bone metastases was 92%.
Conclusions: P1NP seems to be a valuable marker offering additive information to bone scan results.

P-5 Urology

Selective recognition of enzymatically active prostate-specific antigen (PSA) by anti-PSA monoclonal antibodies for diagnostic application

Michel Sandrine, Collomb-Clerc E, Jolivet-Reynaud C
UMR 2714 CNRS/bioMérieux, Lyon, France.

Aims: The purpose of this study was to characterize the properties of two anti-free PSA monoclonal antibodies (mAbs) for the detection of specific prostate cancer-related PSA forms.
Methods: PSA, from seminal fluid, LNCaP supernatant and sera from cancer patients, was immunopurified by these two mAbs (5D3D11 and 6C8D8) as well as by an anti-total PSA mAb. The different immunopurified PSA fractions were analyzed and their respective enzymatic activities were determined.
Results: In seminal fluid, enzymatically active PSA was equally purified with the three mAbs. In LNCaP supernatants and human sera, 5D3D11 immunopurified active PSA mainly, whereas 6C8D8 immunopurified PSA with residual activity. In sera, we identified the presence of a mature inactive PSA form which can be activated into active PSA by use of high saline concentration or capture by an anti-PSA mAb capable of enhancing PSA activity. According to PSA models built by comparative modelling with the crystal structure of horse prostate kallikrein described previously, we assume that active and activable PSA could correspond to mature intact PSA with open and closed conformations of the kallikrein loop. A sandwich assay with 5D3D11 as capture mAb allowed to detect activable PSA in human sera and to discriminate prostate cancer from benign hyperplasia.
Conclusions: mAb 5D3D11 the specificity of which was restricted to both active and activable PSA, is a valuable tool to improve early prostate cancer diagnosis.

P-6 Urology

Prostaglandin $_2$ and prostate-specific antigen blood and prostate secretion level correlation in prostate inflammatory and tumoral diseases

Miroshnikov V, Nikulina Dina , Ivanov P, Seidov K, Polunin A
Dept of Biochemistry, Dept of Urology and Diagnosis Center of State Medical Academy, Astrakhan, Russia

Aims: To determine the level of two organospecific prostate components - Pg 2 and PSA- in sera and prostate secretion of patients with BPH, PC and CHP and the correlation of their levels in the two body fluids. Morphofunctional changes in the gland caused by prostatitis make the differential diagnosis (DD) of CHP and tumor prostate diseases more difficult.
Methods: Pg 2 and PSA has been detected in 228 samples in patient and donor blood sera and prostate secretion (BPH – 94, PC – 54, CHP - 57) by immunoassay. Pg 2 was determined in pg/ml, PSA –in ng/ml.
Results: Our findings confirm previous data that the PSA level in the blood has its peak value in prostate cancer (PC) (49,72±8,6) and much lower and low differing levels in BPH and CHP (4,05±1,05 and 3,42±1,12, correspondingly). Pg 2 level in the blood of all patient groups on the contrary decreases significantly as compared to its level in blood donors (1338,5±68,6) to min M in PC (256,8±19,6). The levels of Pg 2 and PSA in prostate secretion exceed significantly their levels in blood: Pg 2 - from 51006,4±258,5 to 6032,7±72,2; PSA –from 2434,21±77,53 to 2220±912,6. In connexion with the fact that the Pg 2 levels in blood and secretion change in different directions (non-uniformly) the computation of the Pg 2 level rate in secretion and blood (K=ps/bs) strengthen the information density of this index. In blood donors K=9,8, in CHP =61,98 (before the treatment) and 41,03 (after the treatment) In BPH =125,96 (before the treatment) and 34,88 (after it), in PC K=124,94 (before the treatment),101,83 (after the treatment) and 11,72 (after the castration).
Conclusions: Inflammatory and tumoral changes in prostate tissue are reflected in the secretion to the blood of organospecific components and their accumulation in the prostate secretion. Features of secretion and blood Pg $_2$ level changes may be used as a complementary criterion in DD of inflammatory and tumoral prostate processes.

P-7 Urology

Comparative analysis of some humoral components of reactivity in prostate diseases

Nikulina Dina, Miroshnikov V, Ivanov P, Seidov K
Department of Biochemistry, Department of Urology and Diagnosis Center of State Medical Academy, Astrakhan, Russia

Inflammatory diseases and tumor growth induce the activity of blood proteins with cytostatic, cytoregulatory, enzymoregulatory and other effects on the repair of damaged tissues and disturbed homeostasis. Cytokines and acute phase proteins are such proteins.
Aims: To determine pathogenetic and diagnostic role of cytokine and acute phase protein level change in inflammatory and tumor prostate diseases during the treatment.
Methods: We have studied simultaneously cytokines (tumor necrosis factor TNF-α, IL-1α, IL-4) by immunoassay and acute phase proteins (C-reactive protein, alpha2-macroglobulin, pregnancy-associated alpha2-glycoprotein) by the immunodiffusion analysis in 87 samples of patient and blood donor sera in benign prostate hyperplasia (BHP), prostate cancer (PC) and chronic prostatitis (CHP).
Results: It was found that in prostate diseases IL-1α decreases more than half as much (2,46- 2,88), and IL-4 and TNF-α- increase from 1,54 to 4,6 and 1,1 to 2,3 time, correspondingly, as compared to their concentrations in blood donors. The greatest IL-1α decrease is found in BHP and PC, the peak values of IL-4 and TNF-α are found in PC. During successful treatment the level has changed significantly toward normal values. The very interesting data have been obtained about α–MG level, which has been increasing in CHP and has been decreasing significantly in PC.
Conclusions: Non-uniformly directed changes of cytokine and acute-phase protein levels have been detected in blood sera of patients with prostate disease. Dynamic peculiarities of these reactivity proteins' production during the disease development and treatment depend on pathology type and reflect the tension or weakening of their specific pathogenetic link.

P-8 Urology

Characterization of prostate-specific antigen (PSA) binding peptides selected by phage display technology

Ferrieu-Weisbuch C, Michel Sandrine, Ott C, Jolivet-Reynaud C,
UMR 2714 CNRS/bioMérieux, Lyon, France.

Aims: The presence of activable PSA was characterized previously in sera from patients with prostate cancer by use of the specific anti-free PSA monoclonal antibody (mAb) 5D3D11. The purpose of this study is to obtain ligands for the specific recognition of different PSA forms including active or activable PSA.
Methods: Phage-displayed linear and cyclic peptide libraries were screened with PSA coated directly into microplate wells or presented by two different anti-total PSA mAbs, and the selected phages were reproduced as synthetic peptides.
Results: The four selected peptides were found to capture and to detect specifically free PSA, even in complex biological media such as sera or tumor cell culture supernatants. Alanine scanning of peptide sequences showed the involvement of aromatic and hydrophobic residues in the interaction of the peptides with PSA, whereas Spotscan analysis of overlapping peptides covering the PSA sequence identified a peptide binding to the kallikrein loop at residues 82-87 suggesting that the peptides could recognize a non-clipped form of PSA. Moreover, the PSA-specific peptides enhanced the enzymatic activity of PSA immobilized into microplate wells, whereas the capture of PSA by the peptides inhibited totally its enzymatic activity, and the peptide binding to PSA had no effect in solution.
Conclusions: These PSA-specific peptides could be potential tools for the recognition of PSA forms more specifically associated with prostate cancer.

P-9 Urology

The follow-up of patients with bladder carcinoma by combined use of abdominal ultrasound, urinary CYFRA 21-1 and cytology

Nisman Benjamin, Yutkin V, Barak V, Peretz T, Pode D
Oncology and Urology Departments, Hadassah University Hospital, Jerusalem, Israel

Aim: We examined the efficacy of the combined use of three noninvasive diagnostic tests: bladder ultrasound (US), the urinary CYFRA 21-1 and cytology as a potential substitute for cystoscopy in the detection of recurrence of bladder carcinoma (BC).
Methods: 324 urine samples from 157 patients who were under surveillance after transurethral resection of BC were included. All patients underwent US, urine cytology and cystoscopy. Biopsies were obtained if a tumor was seen on cystoscopy or if there was a suspicion of carcinoma in situ. The urinary CYFRA 21-1 was measured by commercial kit. The optimal cut-off for this marker was defined by the ROC analysis.
Results: During follow-up, 26 recurrences were detected by cystoscopy and confirmed by biopsy. US, urinary CYFRA 21-1 and cytology demonstrated a sensitivity of 46.2%, 69.2%, 23.1% and specificity of 99.7%, 68.1%, 97.0%, respectively. The combined use of all three tests revealed 23 recurrent tumor (88.5%). Among patients with all three tests negative (202 of 324), only three had tumor recurrence (pT0G1 tumors measuring less then 5mm in size) resulting in 62% of cystoscopies, that could have been avoided.
Conclusions: the combined use of US, urinary CYFRA 21-1 and cytology is an effective, noninvasive approach for the detection of recurrence of BC and many substitute cystoscopy in more than half of patients during surveillance.

P-10 Urology

Primary tumor as model for androgen depletion of prostate cancer

Bühler Patrick[1], Elsässer U[1], Freudenberg N[2], Wetterauer U[1]
[1]Department of Urology; [2] Department of Pathology, Freiburg , Germany

Aims: Androgen ablation is a standard treatment for patients with advanced prostate cancer. However, after a short clinical response, most tumors progress to an androgen-independent most aggressive phenotype, for which no effective therapies are available. Because there are no relevant *in vitro* models, the aim of present study was to establish primary prostate cancer cultures under normal and androgen-deprived conditions and compare the expression of marker genes as an aid in understanding the molecular alterations induced by androgen deprivation.
Methods: From fresh tumor material with a histopathological confirmed high tumor content, small pieces of 1 to mm^3 were placed on a semipermeable polyethylene terephthalate membrane and covered with PREGM, either with or without 10nM dehydrotestosterone (DHT). The outgrowing cells were characterized according to cytomorphological criteria and by immunocytochemistry. Expression of marker genes was studied by RT-PCR.
Results: After 2 to 4 weeks in culture, cells grew out of the tumor pieces, forming a monolayer. The cells were found to be mainly epithelial. Their malignancy was confirmed by pathocytomorphology. Expression of cytokeratins 5 and 18 revealed the presence of basal as well as luminal cells. The genes for PSMA, c-myc and androgen receptor were differentially expressed in the cultures with and without DHT.
Conclusions: The described primary culture model offers a relevant system for studying global gene expression and may help to identify those genes which are relevant for androgen-independent aggressive prostate cancer.

P-11 Urology

Osteoprotegerin, RANKL, and bioactive testosterone in prostate cancer patients

Tarapacz J, Rychlik U, Kulpa Jan Kanty, Migas B, Byrski E, Stelmach A
Center of Oncology – M.Skłodowska-Curie Memorial Institute, Cracow Division, Poland

Aims: RANKL and osteoprotegerin are known as important regulators of osteoclastogenesis. The aim of presented study was the evaluation of osteprotegerin, RANKL levels and their ratio in prostate cancer patients without or with bone metastases in respect to free and bioactive testosterone levels.
Methods: Osteoprotegerin (OPG), RANKL, PSA, total testosterone, SHBG, prolactin and albumin were determined after treatment in 100 patients with prostate cancer and in a reference group consisting of 56 men. For each patient the OPG to RANKL ratio, free and bioactive testosterone levels, and percentage of free and bioactive testosterone values were calculated.
Results: Compared to the reference group, prostate cancer patients exhibited significantly higher OPG and prolactin levels, OPG/RANKL ratios and significantly lower bioactive testosterone levels and percentages of this hormone fraction but lacked significant differences in RANKL, total testosterone levels and free testosterone. In the group of patients with bioactive testosterone values lower than 40% in comparison to the remaining prostate cancer patients, significantly higher OPG levels and OPG/RANKL ratios were found. There was a reciprocal relationship between OPG as well as the OPG/RANKL ratio and the bioactive testosterone percentage.
Conclusions: In prostate cancer patients changes in bioactive testosterone percentage seem to influence OPG levels and its ratio to RANKL.

P-12 Breast Ca.

Cytokine gene polymorphisms in iranian patients with breast cancer

Behrouz Gharesi-Fard [1], Talei A[2], Kamali-Sarvestani E[1]
[1] Dept.of Immunology, [2] Dept. of Surgery, Shiraz University of Medical Sciences, Shiraz, Iran.

Aims: Cytokines are powerful modulators of the immune system and can produce anti cancer responses by tumor infiltrating lymphocytes (TILs). Since cytokine gene polymorphisms may be associated with different ability for cytokine production, the aim of this study was to investigate the association between cytokine gene polymorphisms and susceptibility to breast cancer.
Methods: Polymorphism in the genes of TNF-alpha (-308 G/A), TNF-beta (+252 G/A) and IFN-gamma (+874 A/T) as Th1 or pro-inflammatory, and also IL-4 (-590 C/T) and IL-10 (-592 C/A, -819 C/T, -1082 A/T) as Th2 cytokines were investigated in the present study. Peripheral blood samples from 275 female breast cancer patients and 320 cancer free controls were used to detect these single nucleotide polymorphisms by PCR.
Results: There were no differences in the TNF-alpha, TNF-beta, IFN-gamma and IL-10 alleles and genotypes frequencies between breast cancer patients and control subjects.
The frequency of IFN-gamma +874 T/T genotype was significantly higher in breast cancer patients compared to those of controls ($P<0.002$; OR=2.03, 95% CI=1.28-3.2).
Conclusions: Our findings indicate that TNF-alpha, TNF-beta, IL-4 and IL-10 polymorphisms are not associated with breast cancer risk. However our result indicate that Iranian women carrying the IFN-gamma +874 T/T genotype may be exposed to an increased risk of breast cancer development.

P-13 Breast Ca.

Evaluation of the predictive significance of serum HER-2/neu (sNeu), CA15-3 and EGFR in metastatic breast cancer (MBC) HER-2/neu positive patients in a Phase IIb study: paclitaxel (PCT) versus PCT + trastuzumab (T)

Zancan Matelda[1], Gasparini G[2], Crivellari D[3], Filippelli G[4], Silingardi V[5], Papaldo P[6], Amadori D[7].
[1]ABO Association, Regional Hospital, Venice; [2] Medical Oncology San Filippo Neri Hospital, Rome; [3] CRO, Aviano; [4] Presidio Ospedaliero, Paola; [5] Università Modena, [6] Istituto Regina Elena, Rome; [7] Ospedale Morgagni-Pierantoni, Forlì, Italy

Aim: to investigate whether basal levels of sNeu, EGFr and CA15-3 and their variation during therapy are associated with best overall response (BOR) or time to progression (TTP) or are predictive of treatment response .
Methods: 101 untreated MBC patients with HER-2/neu 2+/3+ were randomized to receive PCT (Arm A) or PCT+T (Arm B). CA15-3 and sNeu have been evaluated with Bayer ADVIA Centaur System and EGFr with OncogeneScience kit .
Results: there is a significant variation of CA15-3 and sNeu in both treatment arms but neither was associated with clinical response. CA15-3 levels were associated to BOR (p=0.0238) and TTP (p=0.0217). Tissue HER-2/neu expression (tNeu) has the strongest predictive value overpowering that of sNeu and of the variation of CA15-3.
Conclusions: CA15-3 and sNeu showed a significant variation during therapy but neither was associated with clinical response or had a predictive significance. Only CA15-3 levels showed a prognostic significance. tNeu confirmed its strong predictive value for PCT+T overpowering that of sNeu and of the variation of CA15-3.

P-14 Breast Ca.

AIB-1 gene copy number quantified by Real Time PCR is associated with ER positive and HER 2 negative status

Servanton AC[1], Thezenas S[2], Grenier J[1], Rouanet P[3], Lamy Pierre-Jean [1]
[1]Department of Biology, [2]Biostatistics Unit, [3]Department of Surgical Oncology, CRLC Val d'Aurelle Cancer Institute, Montpellier, FRANCE

Aims : AIB1 is an estrogen receptor (ER) co-activator which can reduce the antagonist activity of tamoxifen and could be activated by HER2. We wished to determine AIB1 and HER2 gene amplification levels in primary breast cancer tumor by a Real-Time PCR assay and the correlation with hormonal prognosis factors.
Methods : Human breast cancer cell lines and frozen tumor specimen from 315 patients were selected for the study. The measurement of AIB-1 and HER2 gene amplification was performed on total DNA by Real-Time PCR using respectively GAPDH and SST2 as normalising genes. ER and PR cytosolic functional protein content were quantified by LBA assay.
Results: MCF-7 and T-47D presented respectively a strong (>16fold) and a weak (>2.5 fold) amplification for AIB-1 while the other cells lines were non amplified. HER2 amplification was found in 34 patients (10,8%). AIB-1 amplification (2-6 fold) was found in 3 (0.9%) patients. All of these patients showed ER positive status and HER2 negative status. AIB-1 gene amplification was correlated with HER2 gene non amplification and ER positive status. No correlation was found between AIB-1 amplification and PR status.
Conclusions: Real-Time PCR was successfully performed to detect gene amplification on breast tumor. Targeting 2 genes involving tamoxifen resistance, we have shown that AIB-1 amplification is associated with ER positive and HER2 negative status.

P-15 Breast Ca.

CA 15-3 and CEA in breast cancer patients: relationsship with nodal invasion, tumor size of metastases and receptor status

Buda Francesco, Stimolo A, Bergamo O, Svenda G, D'Agnolo E, *Aragona P,** Buda C,** La Torre F
Med Oncology and Clin Research Laboratory, "City of Udine" Hospital.* Clin Research Laboratory and Micro-biology ASL n 6 FVG Region, Italy ,** Dept of Surgery and Med Oncology University, Messina, Italy

Aims and Methods: To measure CA15-3 and CEA by RIA in breast cancer patients (M0/M+) and to correlate the results with the receptor status and clinical parameters like nodal involvement and metastases,
Results: CA15-3 abnormal levels have been found in 32% pts with M_0 breast cancer(24/75) and in 65% of M_1 cases (65/100).Pts with tumor size T_{3-4} have concentrations of this marker(40%)statistically higher than those found in pts T_{1-2} breast cancer($p<0.05$).This relationship among CA15-3 with nodal invasion and tumor size, makes to think in its possible prognostic value. Pts with disseminated tumor show similar sensitivity with both markers, CA15-3(65%)and CEA(67%) Both parameters are related with site of metastases: the highest levels of both markers were found in pts with liver metastases and the lowest ones in those localized in skin($p<0.001$).No correlation was found between ER and CA15-3 in M_0 pts. By contrast in pts with metastases and ER+(mean 400+/-393 U/ml) CA15-3 levels were higher than in the cases with ER-(mean 58.3 +/- 43.6 U/ml) ($p<0.001$). This differences were most evident with CEA as well in breast cancer M_0 than in breast cancer M_1.
Conclusions: serum CA15-3 is more sensitive than CEA, mainly in M_0 breast cancer, although its specificity seems to be lower than CEA. The serum levels of CA15-3 are related with the tumor extent with the highest values in cancer with metastases.In M_0breast cancer, they are related with nodal involvement and tumor size.In disseminated breast cancer (M_1) CA15-3 is related to sites of metastases being the highest in liver involvement and lowest in skin metastases. CA15-3serum levels seem to be related with the estrogen receptor status in patients with metastases.

P-16 Breast Ca.

VEGF signaling pathways in tamoxifen-resistant breast cancer cells

Scherbakov A, Gershtein Elena G, Lobanova J*, Shishkin A**, Krasil'nikov MA*
Laboratory of Clinical Biochemistry, *Laboratory of Molecular Endocrinology, and **Laboratory of Tumor Cell Genetics, Russian N.N.Blokhin Cancer Research Center, Moscow, Russia

Aims: The aim of this study was to investigate the possible role of vascular endothelial growth factor (VEGF) signaling pathways in tamoxifen-resistant breast cancer cells.
Methods: Western blot and standard ELISA kits were used to detect the protein levels of VEGF, mitogen-activated protein kinase (phospho- ERK1/2) and VEGF receptor 2 (VEGFR-2/KDR) in the parent (MCF-7) and tamoxifen-resistant (MCF-7/TR) breast cancer cell lines. The mRNA expression of VEGFR-2 was analyzed by semi-quantitative RT-PCR.
Results: Using a long-term tamoxifen treatment of MCF-7 breast cancer cells we have developed a tamoxifen-resistant cell subline in which the level of VEGF is partially decreased and is not affected by estrogen or tamoxifen addition. In contrast, VEGFR-2 was significantly increased in MCF-7/TR as compared to MCF-7 cells at both mRNA and protein levels. Treatment of MCF-7 and MCF-7/TR cells with the VEGF inhibitor (soluble fragment of Flt-1/Fc Chimera) demonstrated that the VEGF signaling pathway inhibition resulted in a decrease of ERK1 and ERK2 activities which correlated with the partial decrease of cell growth.
Conclusions: Taken together, these results demonstrate the phenomenon of VEGFR-2 activation in tamoxifen-resistant breast cancer cells, indicating that VEGF/VEGFR-2 signaling pathway may be one of the mechanisms contributing to the maintenance of breast cancer cells' survival by a direct stimulation of tumor cell growth as well as by induction of angiogenesis.

The study was supported by RFBR grants 03-03-32111; 04-04-48458.

P-17 Breast Ca.

Abstract not submitted.

P-18 Breast Ca.

The transketolase protein TKTL1 is overexpressed in breast cancer

Földi Martha[1], Zur Hausen A[2], Bau L[1], Kretz O[3], Watermann D[1], Gitsch G[1], Stickeler E[1], Coy JF[4]
[1]Dept. of Obstetrics & Gynaecology, University of Freiburg, [2]Dept. of Pathology, University of Freiburg, [3]Dept. of Anatomy and Cell Biology, University of Freiburg, [4]R-Biopharm AG, Darmstadt, Germany

Aims: The transketolase protein acts as thiamine dependent key enzyme in the non-oxidative part of the pentose phosphate cycle. Overexpression of the transketolase-like-1 (TKTL1) gene was shown to be associated with poor prognosis and patient outcome in various malignancies.
Here we examined the expression of the TKTL1 protein in breast cancer, as well as its correlation with histopathological data and its possible impact on patients' outcome and survival.
Methods: We performed a retrospective immunohistochemical study on paraffin embedded tissue micro arrays of 129 different breast carcinomas using a TKTL1 specific monoclonal antibody.
A quantitative and a qualitative scoring system was applied.
Results: 113 of the examined breast carcinomas showed specific cytoplasmic staining for TKTL1 (53 weak, 39 moderate, 21 strong staining), whereas 16 tumor samples as well as the majority of corresponding normal breast tissue were TKTL1 negative.
Conclusions: This is the first study to test and identify TKTL1 overexpression in a significant subset of breast carcinomas. Next to its predictive value, the importance of TKTL1 overexpression is underlined by the fact that TKTL1 is a candidate therapeutic target for the treatment of human malignancies.

P-19 Breast Ca.

CA 15-3, BR, CEA, and HER2 serum

Wójcik Ewa, Kruczak A, Mitu J, Stasik Z, Sobolewska K, Kulpa J
Center of Oncology - M.Skłodowska-Curie Memorial Institut, Cracow Division, Poland

Aims: HER2 in epithelial cells plays the main role in a complex signal transduction network that controls cell growth and differentiation. Intensive amplification of this gene and subsequent overexpression of HER2 protein result in oncogenesis. The determination of HER 2 extracellular domain in serum might be useful in the diagnostics of breast cancer patients, and also in monitoring of Herceptin treatment.
The purpose of this study was to estimate the concentration of HER 2 with regard to the cellular expression of this protein as well as to the status of estrogen and progesteron receptors.
Methods: CA 15-3, BR, CEA, and HER2 serum concentrations were determined in 196 breast cancer patients before surgery. For each patient the status of steroid receptors as well as expression of HER2 receptor were assessed by IHC method.
Results: Elevated HER2 serum concentrations were found in 10.7%, CEA in 7.6%, CA 15-3 in 16.8% and BR in 18.4% of breast cancer patients. Unlike CEA and sHER2, the concentrations of CA 15-3 and BR tended to grow with stage of disease. Elevated levels of Ca 15-3 and/or sHER2 appeared in 25.5% of examined patients. Serum HER2 levels were significantly higher in breast cancer patients with ER negative than ER positive status.
Conclusions: Complementary to CA 15-3, the determination of sHER2 seems to increase the diagnostic effectiveness in breast cancer patients.

P-20 Breast Ca.

HER-2 protein concentrations in breast cancer tissue and correlation to clinical disease markers.

Olsen Dorte Aalund, Østergaard B, Wamberg P, Bokmand S, Jakobsen E, Brandslund I
Laboratory Center, Vejle County Hospital and the Faculty of Health Sciences, Odense University, Denmark

Aims: The aim was to investigate, if HER-2 concentrations in breast cancer tissue: 1. can be distinguished from normal breast tissue and 2. are correlated to clinical parameters.
Methods: Fresh tissue samples of malignant and adjacent benign breast tissue were collected from 70 consecutive women admitted for surgical treatment of breast cancer. The tissue samples were forzen at -80°C immediately after removal. The samples were homogenised at 4°C in a lysis buffer and the protein concentration was measured using the BCA protein assay (Pierce, USA). The concentration of HER-2 was measured by ELISA (Oncogene Science, USA) and HER-2 chemiluminescent assay for Advia Centaur (Bayer, USA).
Results: We found higher HER-2 concentrations in cancer tissue (mean 96.7 ng/mg protein) compared to the autologous reference tissue (mean 15 ng/mg protein), ($p<0.00005$). Removing 5 outliers and choosing a 95% reference interval the upper normal limit was 20 ng/mg protein, and 67% of cancers were found positive. No correlation was found to tumour stage, size or sentinel node metastasis.
Conclusions: We found a higher prevalence of HER-2 in cancer tissue using quantitative protein measurements than reported with IHC, FISH or S-HER-2, but no correlation to clinical disease markers. Quantification of HER-2 in tissue could be an aid to diagnosis, and possibly prognosis.

P-21 Breast Ca.

Abstract not submitted.

P-22 Breast Ca.

The use of CEA and CA15-3 for estimation of the clinical status and effectiveness of chemotherapy in metastatic breast cancer patients

Laessig D, Stieber Petra, Heinemann V[1], Untch M[2], Nagel D, Seidel S; Institute of Clinical Chemistry, [1]Medical Department III, [2]Gynecological Department, University of Munich, Germany

Aims: The potential value of tumor markers like CEA and CA 15-3 is well established in follow-up care of breast cancer patients. As a result of a combination of expert knowledge and confidence, the present situation is more to follow their kinetics than to react on their results. Therefore we try to validate the significance of CEA and CA15-3 in the clinical course of metastatic disease.

Patients and Methods: We investigated in 147 breast cancer patients who either had metastasis at time of primary diagnosis (N=28) or developed metastatic lesions during follow-up (N=119). Most patients suffered from more than one site of metastasis. All patients were treated by systemic therapies- endocrine, chemotherapeutic, antibody or combined treatment. CEA (AxSYM/ Abbott) and CA15-3 (Elecsys/ Roche) were mostly determined every 3 or 4 weeks; the therapeutic response was assessed by UICC criteria.

Results: We evaluated CEA and CA15-3 at first diagnosis of recurrence and at every future clinical progression/new metastases. At first time of relapse CEA was elevated in 53.5% above the 95th percentile of healthy individuals and CA 15-3 in 71.8% with an increasing percentage of sensitivity with growing numbers of future events of progressive disease (PD) (2nd PD CEA 54%/CA15-3 71%, 3rd PD 64 %/81%, 4th PD 69%/90%). We also observed a general shift of increasing levels of CEA (ng/ml)/CA 15-3 (U/ml) with the number of events (e.g. the medians 1st PD CEA 2.7/CA 15-3 43.8; 2nd PD 3.0/46.5; 3rd PD 4.1/71.5; 4th PD 5.2/91.5). According to therapy response patients who failed to treatment showed an increase within 3 weeks of both CEA (median 6.0%) and CA 15-3 (median 15.0%) and patients who responded to therapy showed a decrease of CEA (median 7.7%) and CA 15-3 (median 13.7%) within 6 weeks. The marker levels of responders after treatment were significantly lower than the values of patients who failed to treatment (CEA 2.5 ng/ml /CA 15-3 65.4 U/ml vs. 8.4 ng/ml / 140 U/ml).

Conclusions: Our results show both a clear correlation between CEA/CA 15-3 and the number of events as well as a correlation between CEA/CA 15-3 and treatment response.

P-23 Breast Ca.

Advanced detection and measurement of cells on membrane (ADAMCOM) from peripheral blood by laser scanning cytometry (LSC) in early stage breast cancer patients

Sanislo L, Kuliffay P, Galbavy S, Sedlak J, Kausitz J
Department of Pathology, Clinic of Laboratory Methods of Investigation, St. Elizabeth Cancer Institute, Bratislava, Slovakia

Aim: The aim of our study was the potential detection of circulating tumour cells (CTCs) in early stage breast cancer patients. Our approach was cell microfiltration through polycarbonate membrane as a concentration method suitable for CTC selection in peripheral blood. The isolated cells on membrane were further analysed by laser scanning cytometry.
Methods: Sixteen patients were enrolled in the study, of which 13 had early stage breast carcinoma and 3 patients had metastatic breast carcinoma. The analyses were performed from 9 ml of peripheral blood, in one patient blood was drawn twice. Blood samples were taken after adjuvant chemotherapy but prior to adjuvant radiotherapy. The control group consisted of 12 clinically healthy subjects.
Results: In the control group 3 subjects out of 12 had 1 CTC, the mean CTC numbers being 0.25 ± 0.45. In the early stage breast cancer patients 0-36 CTCs were detected (mean 13.9 ± 12.9 CTCs) Eight patients out of 13 had more than 2 CTCs (62%). The ADAMCOM technique is a simple and reproducible method of detection of CTCs in peripheral blood. Sensitivity of the method is 88.5%.
Conclusions: Detection of CTCs seems to be a promising method for the monitoring of adjuvant therapy in early stage breast cancer patients and for the identification of high risk patients in whom elevated numbers of CTSs are persisting following the termination of adjuvant therapy.

P-24 Breast Ca.

Serum MUC1 O-glycans from cancer patients contain the Sialyl Tn antigen

Stephenson Sarah J.[1], Royle L.[2], Dwek R[2]., Robertson J.[1], Barnes A.[3], Chapman C.[1], Rudd P[2].
[1]Breast Surgery, University of Nottingham; [2]Glycobiology Institute, University of Oxford; [3]Oncimmune Ltd, Biocity, Nottingham, UK

Aim: The analysis of the O-linked glycosylation of MUC1 purified from advanced breast cancer patient serum.
Methods: MUC1 has been purified from patient serum using affinity chromatography with NCRC-11. O-glycans were released by hydrazinolysis und fluorescently labeled. Sugars were identified by a combination of Normal Phase HPLC, exoglycosidase digestions and LC-mass spectroscopy.
Results: We have identified the Sialyl Tn (STn) sugar epitope on MUC1 purified from a breast cancer patient serum. STn represented approximately 3.8% of total assigned sugars. The most common sugar was the sialylated core 1 structure NeuNAc 2-3Gal 1-3GalNAc (29.1%), and 1.9% of assigned sugars were core 2 based.
Conclusions: MUC1 and STn are important cancer markers and a correlation between their expression in cancer has previously been reported. Expression of the STn antigen results from sialylation of the core monosaccharide GalNAc, and the antigen has been demonstrated by immunohistochemistry in 84% of breast cancers. However, analysis of MUC1 glycans from MCF-7 and T47D breast cancer cell lines has not confirmed the presence of STn.
Here we have verified the presence of STn on secreted MUC1 purified from patient serum. The STn epitope demonstrates aberrant glycosylation that arisis from sialylation of the core GalNAc. Many factors can alter glycan processing, including upregulation of ST6GalNAc I, - II.

P-25 Cervix Ca.

Squamous cell carcinoma antigen in monitoring uterine cervix cancer patients

Sergeeva NS, Dubovetskaya OB, Marshutina NV, Novikova EG, Demidova LV, Trushina OI
Moscow Hertsen Reseach Oncological Institute, Moscow, Russia

Aims: The aim of the study was to assess the usefulness of serial measurement of squamous cell carcinoma antigen (SCCA) in monitoring utherine cervix cancer patients (UCC).
Methods: SCCA level in serum of 316 patients with UCC in situ and stage I-III (FIGO) have been analyzed by ELISA SCCA kit (Abbott Diagnostics,USA). The discriminative level of SCCA was 1,5 ng/ml. Routine serum SCCA determination was performed at each follow-up visit of patients for 2 years.
Results: Elevated serum SCCA concentrations were found:3,9% (2/52) UCC in situ, 28,9% (16/55), 76,9% (30/39), 85,7% (72/84) of patients with UCC stage I-III (respectively). The stabilization of SCCA level took place within one week after operation and 4-6 weeks after completion of radiotherapy. For patients with elevated SCCA posttreatment levels the further progression of disease had been proven, 15,8 % (50/316) patients had recurrence within 2 years. SCCA levels were elevated in 82% (41/50) patients (mean SCCA :15,8 ± 5,0ng/ml (0,2-227,8)). The median lead time for SCCA was 4,3±0,6 months (2-10). The mean velocity of SCCA growth was 3,8 ng/ml/month (0,1-11,2). Two patients with initially negative SCCA levels had demonstrated the elevation of antigen during progression of disease. The nonspecific causes of elevated SCC level in serum of disease-free patients were analyzed.
Conclusions: Pretreatment serum SCC antigen levels can be used to identify patients with a poor prognosis. Serial serum levels of SCCA gives the evidence for early detection of recurrence or disease progression. This marker might also be useful for monitoring the treatment effects of UCC patients.

P-26 Cervix Ca.

Tumor markers in patients with cervical cancer

Kotowicz Beata[1], Fuksiewicz M[1], Kowalska M[1], Kami ska J[1], Bidzi ski M[2]
[1] Department. of Tumor Markers, [2]Department of Gynecologic Oncology, Cancer Centre and Institute of Oncology, Warsaw, Poland

Aims: The purpose of this study was to evaluate the potential use of assessments of serum levels of SCC alone and in combination with CEA, CA125 or IL-6 to improve the diagnosis of cervical cancer.
Methods: The study comprised 175 untreated patients with cervical cancer staged according to FIGO classification. Concentrations of tumor markers were determined using the Abbott instruments system and IL-6 by the ELISA of R&D. For the statistical analysis Mann-Whitney U tests, Kruskall-Wallis ANOVA and Spearman rank correlation method were applied.
Results: The sensitivity of SCC assessment in patients with stage I-IIA cervical cancer proved to be low (36%), but concomitant determination of SCC and CA 125, CEA or IL-6 increased the diagnostic sensitivity up to 45%, 51% and 68%, respectively. The levels of all tumor markers and IL-6 correlated with clinical stage. SCC related to histological type, with significantly higher levels in squamous cell carcinomas than in adenocarcinomas ($p<0,02$). No relationships between serum levels of tumor markers or IL-6 with the histological grade and patients' age were found.
Conclusions: Determination of serum levels of SCC in combination with CEA, CA 125 or IL-6 in particular, as compared to the assessment of SCC alone, is potentially more effective in the diagnosis of cervical cancer, especially in the early stage patients.

P-27 Gynecological Ca.

Co-expression of hCG and LH/hCG receptors in gynecological cancer tissues

Jankowska Anna, Andrusiewicz M, Grabowski J, *Nowak-Markwitz E, Szczerba A, Warchol JB,
Dept. of Cell Biology, *Division of Obstetric & Gynecology, University of Medical Sciences, Poznan, Poland

Aims: Analysis of the LH/hCGR receptor expression in gynecological cancer tissues (ovarian, endometrial and uterine cervix) as a potential mediator of hCG action.
Methods: Conventional RT-PCR method and sequence specific primers were used to establish gene expression on the RNA level. The mRNA expression of *hCG* and *LH/hCG* receptor was analyzed in 29 patients with histologically confirmed cancer.
Results: The obtained results showed the co-expression of *LH/hCG* receptors and *hCG* in 22 studied cancer tissues. In 7 studied cases the *LH/hCG* receptor transcripts were not detected, however the expression of *hCGβ* as well as the house keeping gene *β-actin* were shown.
Conclusions: Since 76% of cases investigated showed co-expression of *hCGβ* and *LH/hCG* receptor, it may be supposed that the mechanism of uncontrolled growth of cancer cells could be related to the action of hCG via LH/hCG receptor expressed in the same tissue. The detection of *LH/hCG* mRNA in only 76% of the study cases can be explained by an alternative splicing of pre-mRNA or sensitivity of the method used for LH/hCGR detection, rather than by the lack of expression of the study gene. This finding could be relevant for an understanding of the growth control mechanisms in gynecological cancer cells.

P-28 Gynecological Ca.

Expression of *hCG* and *LH/hCG* receptors in endometrial cancer cells

Andrusiewicz Miroslaw, Jankowska A, Szczerba A, *Nowak-Markwitz E, Warchol JB
Dept. of Cell Biology, *Division of Obstetric & Gynecology, University of Medical Sciences, Poznan, Poland

Aims: The localization of hCG and LH/hCG expression in endometrial hyperplasia and cancer.
Methods: The expression and distribution of hCG and LH/hCG• was assessed by *in situ* RT-PCR and immunohistochemistry methods. The receptor's presence was analyzed in 8 patients with histologically confirmed endometrial cancer, hyperplasias with atypia (3 cases) and without atypia (2 cases) as well as in 4 specimens of endometrium without any pathological changes and 2 placentas.
Results: In all studied specimens of the endometrial carcinoma and hyperplasia with atypia the active *hCG* gene was found. Noncancerous tissue as well as hyperplasia without atypia demonstrated lack of the gene expression. The transcripts of *LH/hCG* receptor was observed only in half of the study cases. The distribution of study gene's products was different. Not all cells of analyzed tissue revealed the presence of the active genes. hCG was found in the basal layer of endometrium, whereas LH/hCG was localized in the glandular epithelium.
Conclusions: The obtained results clearly show that the presence of *hCG* active gene is a marker of oncogenesis. It may be supposed that the mechanism of uncontrolled growth of cancer cells depends on the action of hCG via LH/hCG receptors expressed in the same tissue.

P-29 Gynecological Ca.

Expression and polymorphisms of aryl hydrocarbon receptor and cytochrome P450 1A1 genes in endometrial cancer

Michalak M[1], Rubi B[2], Malkowska Walczak B[1], Nowak-Markwitz Ewa[1], Paczy ski M[1], Trzeciak WH[2]
[1]Department of Gynaecological Oncology, Department of Obstetrics and Gynaecology;
[2]Department of Biochemistry and Molecular Biology, University of Medical Sciences, Poznan, Poland

Aims: 1. Investigation of *CYP1A1* and *AhR* expression in endometrial cancer, 2. Correlation between the level of expression and the tumour FIGO stage, 3. Evaluation of possible association between *CYP1A1, AhR* polymorphisms and endometrial cancer.
Methods: Study group consisted of 57 patients with endometrial cancer in different FIGO stages. Control group contained 35 patients. Total RNA and DNA were isolated from the tissue samples, reverse transcribed to cDNA and amplified by RT-PCR (*LightCycler* System). Polymorphic variants were detected by PCR-RFLP.
Results: The expression of *CYP1A1* was lower in endometrial cancer cells than in the normal endometrium [p<0.001] and negatively correlated with FIGO stage. The level of *AhR* expression was also lower in endometrial cancer cells [p= 0.016] and negatively correlated with FIGO stage of the disease [= -0.19, p=0.03]. Arg554Lys *AhR* variant was detected in 69% of specimens from the study group. In the control group the wild type of *AhR* prevails (^{2}=6.93, p=0.008). Diagnostic odds ratio for searched *AhR* polymorphism reached 4.75 [95%CI:1.44-15.7].
Conclusions: 1. Lower *AhR* expression in endometrial cancer may affect the level of *CYP1A1* and thus diminish the ability to inactivate potent oestrogens. 2. The capacity to inactivate potent oestrogens in endometrial cancer is decreasing during its development and progression. 3. Carrier of an investigated *AhR* variant is at 5-times higher risk of endometrial cancer than the carrier of a wild type of *AhR*.

P-30 Ovary Ca.

The expression of maspin in ovarian cancer

Tarkowski Rafal, Polak G, Nowakowski A, Wertel I, Kotarski J
1st Department of Gynecology, University School of Medicine, Lublin, Poland

Aims: of the study were to determine the expression of maspin in benign and malignant ovarian neoplasm. Ovarian cancer is one of the leading causes of death among gynecologic malignancies. However, molecular and genetic events, associated with early ovarian cancer development still remain enigmatic. Maspin (mammary serpin) is a member of the serine protease inhibitor superfamily. There are several lines of evidence that maspin may play a crucial role in cancer prevention as well as in normal embryonical development.
Methods. Specimens of 16 benign ovarian cysts and 16 cystadenocarcinomas of the ovary were obtained. Maspin expression was determined by immunohistochemistry. Staging of ovarian cancer was performed according to FIGO.
Results. Immunohistochemistry revealed that maspin expression was cytoplasmic in both benign and malignant ovarian neoplasms. No positive staining was observed in nuclei of the studied samples. No significant difference in maspin expression was found between studied samples. We did not find significant correlation between maspin expression and age or FIGO stage in women with ovarian cancer.
Conclusions. We demonstrated, for the first time, that maspin is expressed in follicle ovarian cysts. However, further studies are still needed to clarify the role of maspin in ovarian carcinogenesis.

The study was supported by the State Committee for Scientific Research, Warsaw, Poland, grant 3PO5E 01824

P-31 Ovary Ca.

Presence of dendritic cells in the ascites of women with ovarian cancer

Wertel I[1], Polak G[1], Roli ski J[2], Tarkowski R[1], Kotarski J[1]
[1]1st Department of Gynecology and [2]Department of Clinical Immunology, University School of Medicine, Lublin, Poland.

Aims: The aim of our study was to estimate the myeloid and lymphoid dendritic cells (DCs) in the ascites of women with ovarian cancer.
Methods: We examined 34 patients with ovarian cancer and 29 women with serous cystadenoma. DCs were isolated from peritoneal fluid (PF), stained with monoclonal antibodies: anti-BDCA-1 and anti-CD-19 or anti-BDCA-2 and anti-CD123 and estimated using flow cytometry.
Results: PF myeloid DCs constituted 0.73% of mononuclear cells in patients with ovarian cancer and 8.52% in women with serous cystadenoma. The percentage of myeloid DCs was higher in women with serous cystadenoma in comparison to patients with ovarian cancer. Lymphoid DCs constituted 0,9% in women with ovarian cancer and 0.12% in patients with serous cystadenoma. The percentage of lymphoid DCs was higher in patients with ovarian cancer than in women with serous cystadenoma. Significantly higher BDCA-1/BDCA-2 DCs ratio in PF of patients with serous cystadenoma in comparison with ovarian cancer patients was found.
Conclusions: It seems possible that decreased BDCA-1/BDCA-2 dendritic cells ratio in patients with ovarian cancer may favour Th2 lymphocyte differentiation and/or induction of immunological tolerance in these women.

This work was supported by a grant from Committee of Scientific Research KBN No. 2 PO5E 120 27

P-32 Ovary Ca.

Abstract not submitted.

P-33 Ovary Ca.

Abstract not submitted.

P-34 Ovary Ca.

Abstract not submitted.

P-35 Ovary Ca.

YB-1 expression in ovarian neoplasms

Polak Grzegorz, Tarkowski R, Nowakowski A, Wertel I, Kotarski J
1st Department of Gynecology, University School of Medicine, Lublin, Poland

Unfavourable prognosis of ovarian cancer is due to prompt progression, advanced stage at time of diagnosis and chemoresistance. No protein tissue prognosticators of ovarian cancer are in clinical use yet. YB-1 belongs to a family of "cold shock proteins" and participates at gene expression control at several levels. High expression of YB-1 in tumour tissue correlates with unfavourable prognosis and chemoresistance in some malignant neoplasms.
Aims: to determine the expression of YB-1 in benign and malignant ovarian neoplasms and to correlate the expression of YB-1 with clinical indicators of cancer progression.
Methods: Specimens of 11 benign ovarian cysts and 14 cystadenocarcinomas of the ovary were obtained.YB-1 expression was determined by immunohistochemistry. Staging of ovarian cancer was performed according to FIGO.
Results: Mean YB-1 expression levels in benign and malignant tumours were 5.36 ± 4.1 and 2.86 ± 4.18 points respectively and were not significantly different (p=0.18). No correlation between FIGO stage and expression of YB-1 was found in the group of ovarian cancers, either (p=0.32).
Conclusions: This study demonstrates that YB-1 is expressed both in benign and malignant ovarian tumours. Further studies including larger groups of cases are necessary to elucidate the role of YB-1 in ovarian cancer progression.

The study was supported by State Committee for Scientific Research, Warsaw, Poland, grant 3PO5E 01824.

P-36 Ovary Ca.

Human autoantibodies to CA 125

Allen Claire L, Robertson J, Murray A, Chapman C
Division of Breast Surgery, University of Nottingham, UK

Aims: To identify differences between normal and tumour-associated CA125 and show that mouse antibodies cannot discriminate between these two forms. Further, to demonstrate that human derived autoantibodies to CA125 can distinguish between normal and tumour-associated CA125.
CA125 is a tumour marker routinely measured in the sera of advanced ovarian cancer patients, using mouse monoclonal antibodies to monitor disease progression. In primary disease however, mouse antibodies cannot discriminate between normal and tumour-associated antigen, so a more specific screening modality is required.
Methods: CA125 antigen from normal (1) and cancer sources (3) were affinity purified using a mouse monoclonal antibody, VK-8, bound to CNBr sepharose. CA125 autoantibodies were affinity purified from a breast cancer patient pleural effusion, using CA125 (OVCAR-3) immobilized to CarboLink™ coupling gel (Pierce). Human and mouse antibody specificity to CA125 antigens were compared in ELISA experiments.
Results: It has been demonstrated that breast cancer derived autoantibodies reproducibly bind with higher reactivity to tumour derived CA125 (ovarian or breast) compared to normal CA125, whereas the mouse antibody (VK-8) binds with similar reactivity to both. Furthermore, the sensitivity of the autoantibodies for tumour-associated CA125 is much greater than that observed for the mouse monoclonal VK-8 antibody. These results have also been seen for another mucin, MUC1.
Conclusions: Autoantibodies may therefore be paramount in differentiating between benign and malignant disease, to allow for earlier diagnosis and subsequently increase overall patient survival.

P-37 Ovary Ca.

Combination of ovarian tumors markers

Prokopenko PG, Borisenko SA, Terentiev Alexander
Department of Biochemistry & Department of Obstetrics and Gynecology, Russian State Medical University, Moscow, Russia

Aims: Remarkable feature of ovarian tumors evolution is the early tumor dissemination (peritoneum implantants): on the stage of benign tumors (BT) - 8.4-29%; borderline tumors (BorT) - 50-80%; ovarian cancer (OC) - 95-97%. However, recurrences (REC) of are not usual for BT and patients do not die, whereas in case of BorT recurrences mortality among the patients is 40-44%. In case of OC the tumor cells are resistant to treatment and all patients die from REC during 3 years (Vinokurov V., 2003). Early tumor dissemination and resistance to treatment require immunological diagnosis of tumors at very early stages of the disease.
Methods: Immunochemistry. The presented combination of 3 tumor markers meets the requirements.
Results: The markers were selected from the set of 26 proteins determined an studied using polyclonal antibodies (including CA125 antigen) in case of OC: SOVA-1, protein BT (PBT-40) and ferritin (FER). SOVA-1 is determined (at concentration more than 1 mg/l) in the blood of 25% BT patients, in the blood of all 8 (100%) BorT patients and 75% of OC patients. PBT-40 (1 mg/l) is determined in 25% of healthy donors, in 98% of BT patients and is not determined in OC cases. FER (at concentration more than 200 mkg/l) is determined in 57% of BT cases, in 100% of BorT cases and in 92% of OC cases. Serum levels of SOVA-1 and FER (more slowly) are decreased after successful treatment and are increased again in case of REC.
Conclusions: This combination has an informative value at all stages of the ovarian cancer development. Additional determination of CA125 antigen can indicate for wide dissemination of cancer.

P-38 Ovary Ca.

Relations between HER-2/neu overexpression and its concentration in sera, cyst and ascitic fluids of patients with ovarian carcinoma

Harlozinska Anna, Sedlaczek P, Sobanska E
Department of Clinical Immunology, Wroclaw Medical University, Wroclaw, Poland

Aims: HER-2/neu is a tyrosine kinase receptor associated with signal transduction pathway. The aim of the study was the comparison of HER-2/neu expression in tissue sections and/or respective tumor effusion cells with the concentration of marker in sera, cyst and/or ascitic fluids of patients with histologically different ovarian carcinomas.
Methods: The expression of HER-2/neu was evaluated immunohistochemically and the concentration of marker was measured using commercial enzyme immunoassay (ELISA).
Results: The heterogeneity in HER-2/neu expression in tissue and different concentrations of circulating marker in individual patients were revealed. For the first time a significantly higher values of HER-2/neu in tumor effusions than in corresponding patients sera were detected. In the contrary to the sera, the concentration of HER-2/neu in tumor effusions appeared to be more associated with its expression in tumor tissue.
Conclusions: HER-2/neu tumor tissue overexpression, especially accompanied by high concentration of this receptor in tumor effusions permit to select the subgroup of patients with more aggressive clinical course of the disease. Our results also suggest the possibility of application the different inhibitors of tyrosine kinase receptors for treatment of these group of patients.

P-39 Ovary Ca.

Free ß-subunit of human chorionic gonadotropin as a prognostic factor in ovarian cancer patients

Nowak-Markwitz Ewa[1], Jankowska A[2], Grabowski J[1], Drews K[1], Spaczy ski M[1]
[1]Dept. Gynecology Oncology and [2]Cell Biology , University of Medical Sciences, Poznan, Poland

The expression of the ß-subunit of human chorionic gonadotropin (free hCGß) is a common feature of ovarian cancer tissue, irrespective of tumor histology, grading and FIGO stage.
AIM: The aim of this study was to estimate the frequency of serum free hCGß elevation in patients with ovarian cancer (OC) and to assess its possible prognostic role with regard to survival.
Methods: A total of 76 OC patients entered the study. Free hCGß (nicked and non-nicked) activity was measured by Immulite Sequential Immunometric Assay (DPC, Los Angeles, CA, USA) before treatment.
Results: The elevation of free hCGß (analytical sensitivity of assay 0,02 ng/mL) was found in 65 (86%) women. We have shown that serum concentrations of free hCGß have been higher in FIGO III stage women in comparison to early stage OC (p=0.0008). Logistic regression analysis has proved that pretreatment levels of free hCGß did not differ significantly for platinum-sensitive and platinum-resistant patients. All patients with pretreatment serum lack of free hCGß have been surviving 24 months without recurrence of disease, irrespective of FIGO stage and tumor type and grade. The size of free hCGß was not a predictive factor of disease recurrence and survival.
Conclusion: Serum concentrations of free hCGß cannot be used as a prognostic factor of ovarian cancer outcome.

P-40 Ovary Ca.

The transketolase protein TKTL1 is overexpressed in ovarian carcinoma

Földi Martha[1], Zur Hausen A[2], Jäger M[1], Bau L[1], Kretz O[3], Watermann D[1], Gitsch G[1], Stickeler E[1], Coy J.F[4]
[1]Dept. of Obstetrics and Gynaecology, University of Freiburg, [2]Dept. of Pathology, University of Freiburg, [3]Anatomy and Cell Biology, University of Freiburg, [4]R-Biopharm AG, Darmstadt, Germany

Aims: The transketolase protein acts as thiamine dependant key enzyme in the non-oxidative part of the pentose phosphate cycle. Overexpression of transketolase-like-1 (TKTL1) gene was shown to be associated with poor patient outcome in various malignancies. Here we examined the expression of TKTL1 protein in ovarian carcinomas, as well as its correlation with histopathological data and its possible impact on patients outcome and survival.
Methods: We performed a retrospective immunohistochemical study on paraffin embedded sections of 35 different ovarian carcinomas using a monoclonal antibody specific for TKTL1. A semi- quantitative scoring system was applied.
Results: From 30 invasive ovarian carcinomas 29 displayed a specific staining for TKTL1, only one carcinoma (mucinous cystadenocarcinoma) showed no specific staining. 5 carcinomas were strongly (score 3), 9 moderately (score 2) and 15 weekly (score 1) stained. Among the 5 borderline lesions, 2 cases expressed TKTL1, 3 were negative. In normal ovarian tissue no specific staining for TKTL1 could be detected.
Conclusions: In this first immunohistochemical analysis of the expression of TKTL1 protein in ovarian cancer we found a positive cytoplasmatic staining in 29/30 invasive cases. All normal ovarian tissues and 3/5 borderline lesions showed no staining.

P-41 Gastrointestinal Ca..

CD25+, sIL 2R and Fas R in pheripheral blood (PB) of colorectal cancer (CRC) patients

Donina Simona[1], Jaunalksne I[2], Engele L[1], Smirnova T[1]
[1]Latvian Oncology Center, [2]P. Stradina Clinical University Hospital, Riga, Latvia

Aims: With the aim to evaluate cellular immune response during course of disease and influence of surgery we examined 42 patients at various stages of CRC.
Methods: CD3+, CD4+, CD8+, CD16+, CD25+, CD95+ (Fas R), CD95L+ (Fas L) cells were determined in PB using laser flow cytofluorimeter. sIL 2R was determined in patients serum by a chemiluminiscent immunoassay. Blood samples were collected before any treatment and 12-14 days after surgery.
Results: Significant decrease of CD4+ cells and elevated number of CD95+ cells were obtained in advanced stage of CRC before surgery. Absolute number of CD25+ cells was similar in both groups (local and advanced CRC) but level of sIL 2R in serum was higher in advanced CRC patients. Number of CD4+ cells became slightly elevated after surgery in both groups as well as CD25+ cells. Number of Fas R bearing cells was still elevated in advanced CRC group whereas number of Fas L bearing cells was similar in both groups. Level of sIL 2R after surgery was decreased.
Conclusions: Our results showed a depression of the inductor phase of T cell immune response in advanced CRC patients before surgery and activation of CD4+ cells after tumor removal. Persistant elevation of number of CD95+ cells in advanced CRC showed the prevalence of apoptotic processes in PB lymphocytes. Determination of CD95+, CD95L+, CD25+ cells in PB and sIL 2R in serum may be useful for evaluation of cellular immune response with the aim to understand individual reaction to tumor treatment and course of disease in CRC patients.

P-42 Gastrointestinal Ca.

Preoperative prognosis of colorectal cancer – a pilot study

Visokai Vladimir, Topol an O, Holubec L, Lipská L, Karliková M, Levý M
Department of Surgery of Thomayer Teaching Hospital; 1st Faculty of Medicine Charles University, Prague, Czech Republic

Aims: To find the clinical importance of cytokeratines, thymidine kinase and adhesive molecules in colorectal cancer.
Methods: Serum levels of cytokeratines were determined by IRMA methods (TPS: IDL Sweden, TPA: Biomedica, Italy, CYFRA 21-1: Schering France). Simultaneously other following tumor markers were examined: CA 19-9 and CEA using chemiluminiscence (Beckman, USA). Serum levels of the studied parameters were preoperatively examined in 44 patients with colorectal cancer. Results of tumor markers were correlated with the surgery findings (pTNM, grading).
Results: Cytokeratines were elevated in patients stage III and IV and there was statistic significance of correlation with CEA and CA 19-9 ($p<0.001$). Correlation coefficients were low ($r=0.4-0.7$), which show evidence of independence of the studied parameters. Thymidine kinase and adhesive molecules had low sensitivity and specificity.
Conclusions: This pilot study shows a possibility of improvement in estimation of prognosis in the treatment of patients with colorectal cancer based on a combination of CEA and CA 19-9 with cytoskeleton markers. This conclusion seems promissing when confirmed in a multicenter study.

P-43 Gastrointestinal Ca.

Vascular endothelial growth factor serum level : a marker for recurrence in rectal cancer treated with preoperative radiotherapy

Lamy Pierre-Jean [1], Thezenas S[2],Lemanski C[3],Senesse P[4],Rouanet P[5],Ychou M[4],Grenier J[1], Azria D[3]
[1]Department of Biology, [2]Biostatistics Unit, [3]Department of Radiation Oncology, [4]Department of Medical Oncology, [5]Department of Surgical Oncology, CRLC Val d'Aurelle Cancer Institute, Montpellier, France

Aims : We wished to ascertain whether a correlation existed between the overexpression of VEGF and treatment outcome in a group of patients with rectal adenocarcinoma who had undergone preoperative radiotherapy and total mesorectal resection.
Methods : 54 serum VEGF levels were measured using the Calbiochem Human ELISA kit (QIA51, Merck Biosciences, Darmstadt, Germany). The statistical analyses included logistic regression for determining odds ratios for the development of locoregional recurrences.
Results: Median age was 65 years (range: 32-87). Initial staging showed 76% and 24% stage II and III tumors. RT consisted of 44-Gy pelvic irradiation. Concomitant chemotherapy was used in 18.5% of the cases. Median VEGF level was 280 (range: 79-1811). In a median follow-up of 45.3 months (range: 0.5-104), locoregional recurrence rates was 11% for patients presenting with a VEGF level superior to 280. To date, no recurrence was observed in patients with a VEGF inferior to 280. The corresponding locoregional-free survival rate at four years was 84% (CI 95%, 56-95) and 100%, respectively (p=0.05).
Conclusions: VEGF serum level impacts on locoregional recurrence in locally advanced rectal cancer. Knowledge of VEGF serum level in rectal cancer could contribute to the identification of patients with an increased risk of recurrences.

P-44 Gastrointestinal Ca.

Estimation of metastatic site selectiveness of CEA and CA 19-9 in patients affected by metastasized colorectal carcinoma

Buda Francesco, Stimolo A,Bergamo O, Svenda G, D'Agnolo E, *Aragona P,** Buda C,** La Torre F
Medical Oncology and Clinical Research Laboratory, "City of Udine" Hospital.* Clinical Research Laboratory and Microbiology ASL n 6 FVG Region, Italy ,** Dept of Surgery and Medical Oncology University, Messina, Italy

Aims: The use of these tumorous indicators in clinical practice is confirmed by numerous controlled clinical investigations and our work proved their correlation with metastatic sites in patients affected by metastatized colorectal carcinoma as diagnosed by histology.
Methods: From January 2001 to December 2003, 60 patients who underwent radical surgery for colorectal neoplasm at metastatic stage, confirmed by radiologic, endoscopic and histologic examinations, were monitored.
Results:

Number of patients	Metastatic site	CEA	CA 19-9
39	Liver	34/39 (87,1%)	30/39 (76,9%)
32	Other sites lynph, pul, per	21/32 (65,6%) p>0,05-X2= 3,524	5/32(23,8%) p>0,001-X2=24,028

Conclusions: CEA confirmed its high sensitivity without specific quality of metastatic site. Although being less sensitive than CEA, CA19.9 showed a remarkable selectivity for hepatic metastasis. All together, the combined use of the two indicators was of great help in the clinical evaluation of these patients.

P-45 Gastrointestinal Ca.

Fecal pyruvat kinase M2 (Tumor-M2PK) measurement is a specific screening tool for colorectal cancer (CRC) in a population of 1906 persons in a health care check up setting

Ewald N, Schaller M, Bayer M, Akinci A, Bretzel RG, Kloer HU, Hardt PD
3rd Med. Dept., Giessen University Hospital, Giessen, Germany

Aims: Colonoscopy is supposed to be the best screening tool for CRC but the acceptance in the population is very poor. Therefore, evaluation of additional screening tools is necessary. The measurement of fecal Tumor-M2PK concentrations might be useful in CRC screening. In this study we investigated this marker in 1906 persons undergoing a health care check up.
Methods: Persons undergoing a health care check up provided stool samples for the measurement of fecal Tumor-M2PK concentrations. A commercial available ELISA (ScheBo Biotech AG, Germany) was used.
Results: In 1906 persons participating in a health care check up, mean Tumor-M2PK levels were 1.63 (SEM+/-0.08) U/ml, the median being 0.29 (SD+/-3.68). 1431 persons had levels < 2 U/ml, another 292 < 4 U/ml. Using 4.0 U/ml as a cut off level (as suggested in recent studies) 90.4% of the persons had normal results, while 9.6% had elevated levels.
Conclusions: Since some cases of CRC or adenoma must be suspected in the study population, the specificity of the marker can be supposed to be > 90.4%. The sensitivity ranges about 78-80% for CRC, 60% for polyps > 1 cm. Tumor-M2PK appears to be a helpful tool to characterise persons at risk of CRC, which will then have to be submitted to colonoscopy.

P-46 Gastrointestinal Ca.

Expression of cyclooxygenase-2 (COX-2) and p53 protein in neoplastic progression of Barrett's esophageal mucosa

Slesak Barbara[1], Harlozinska A[1], Szteliga D[1] Rabczynski J[2]
[1]Dept. Clin. Immunol., [2]Dep. Pathol. Anat., Wroclaw Medical University, Wroclaw, Poland

Aims: The evaluation of the expression of two biomarkers contributing to esophageal carcinogenesis.
Methods: Paraffin-embedded specimens from 28 patients with Barrett's esophagus (BE) including adjacent mucosa and 31 with esopahgeal adenocarcinoma (EA) were examined by EnVision immunohistochemistry with application anti- COX-2 and anti- p53 (DO7) monoclonal antibodies. The expression of these markers was scored as low (5-10% of positive cells), moderate (11-40%) and high (above 40% of positive cells).
Results: Heterogenous epithelial expression of COX-2 protein was detected in 64% of BE, however, some differences in percentage of reactive cells were observed. COX-2 protein in adjacent normal esophageal mucosa taken from BE was detectable only in two cases. COX-2 expression was low, moderate or high in 8% (1/12), 33% (4/12) and 58% (7/12) of the EA specimens, respectively. p53 expression was found in 15% of BE and 42% of EA (p=0,03). In BE p53 + cells were detectable in 4/4 cases, and only in one case (1/4) of adjacent normal esophageal epithelium. p53 expression was detected in 13/31 EA cases and the high staining was observed in majority of specimens.
Conclusions: Both COX-2 and p53 expression were detectable at an early stage of Barrett•s esophagus. The detection of these biomarkers may aid in the evaluation of abnormalities in the progression of Barrett's esophagus to adenocarcinoma, indicating the patients with higher risk of cancer development.

P-47 Gastrointestinal Ca.

Quantitative Estimation of MMP-2, MMP-7 and TIMP-1, TIMP-2 in Colorectal Carcinoma Tissue Samples

Rupert Karel[1], Pešta M[2], Holubec L Jr[2], Holubec L[1], Topol an O[2], T eška V[1]
[1]Dept. of Surgery, University Hospital Pilsen,
[2]Central Isotopic Lab., Charles University Pilsen, Czech Republic

Aims: The aim of our study was to assess the levels of MMP-2, MMP-7, TIMP-1 and TIMP-2 mRNA expression in colorectal carcinoma tissue samples and to correlate it with the stage of the disease.
Methods: The study included samples of tumor tissue of 38 patients with colorectal carcinoma and samples of tissue of 11 patients with benign disease. The expression levels of mRNA MMP-2, MMP-7, TIMP-1, TIMP-2 and glyceraldehyde-3-phosphate dehydrogenase (GAPDH) as housekeeping gene were quantified in tissue samples using the method of reverse transcription real-time PCR.
Results: It was found that the level of mRNA expression of MMP-2, MMP-7 and TIMP-1 was significantly higher in tumor tissue samples than in the control tissue ($p<0.0005$, $p<0.0007$ and $p<0.0004$). In addition it was found that the presence of mRNA MMP-2, MMP-7, TIMP-1 and TIMP-2 in tumor tissue samples in these parameters was significantly higher than in the control tissue ($p<0.003$, $p<0.0001$, $p<0.0001$ and $p<0.05$).
Conclusions: The pilot study demonstrated that a significant difference in the level and in the presence of mRNA MMP-2, MMP-7 and TIMP-1 expression between tumor colorectal tissue and control colorectal tissue might be helpful for the prognosis of colorectal cancer.

This work was supported by the grant IGA NR 7894-3.

P-48 Gastrointestinal Ca.

CEA and CA19-9 in patients with colorectal cancer operated in a single institution – retrospective study

Ludmila Lipska, Visokai V[1], Levy M[1], Kormunda S[1]
[1]Department of Surgery of Thomayer Teaching Hospital, 1st Faculty of Medicine Charles University, Prague, Czech Republic

Aims: To evaluate the correlation between preoperative CEA and CA19-9 and pTNM stage of patients operated for colorectal cancer in a single institution.
Methods: Preoperative CEA and CA19-9 were investigated (FPIA Abbott AxSYM) in 584 patients and compared with the pTNM stage. CEA and CA19-9 as prognostic factors were studied.
Results: CEA was in 31% of patients in stage I and II above cut-off level . In stage III CEA was elevated in 48% of patients and in stage IV in 72%. CA19-9 was elevated in stage I and II in 13% of patients and in stage III in 24% and in stage IV in 53%. Both CEA and CA19-9 were below cut-off level in stage I and II in 63%, in stage III in 50% and in stage IV in 23 %. In this group preoperative level of both markers is a statistically significant prognostic factor (p-value = < 0.0001), but in subgroup following R0 surgery is a p-value = 0.069 in CA19-9 and in CEA is p-value = 0.298.
Conclusions: the percentage of patients with elevated markers corresponds to pTNM stage, normal level do not exclude advanced disease. Relevance of markers as a prognostic factor is influenced not only by biological activity of tumor but also by radicality of surgery.

P-49 Gastrointestinal Ca.

Expression of gastric Muc5ac mucin during rat colon carcinogenesis locally induced with MNNG

Murin Nicole[1], Forgue Lafitte M-E[2], Zimber A[3], Bara J[2]
[1]Laboratoire d'histologie, [2]U-673 INSERM, Hôpital St-Antoine, Paris, France; [3]Hebrew University of Jerusalem, Rehovot, Israel

Aims: We studied the expression of Muc5ac mucin during rat colon carcinogenesis induced by intra-rectal deposition of MNNG, a model to evaluate the influence of nutriments in the prevention of colon cancer.
Methods: Colon tumors were induced in 95 rats by intra-rectal administration of MNNG. Groups of rats were sacrificed 2 weeks (n=10), 1 month (n=9) 2, 3, 5 (n=20) and 15 months (n=16) after the treatment. Three groups of 10 rats fed a diet containing 2% Ursodeoxycholate (URSO) were sacrificed the 2, 3 to 5th months. Aberrant Crypt Foci (ACF) were counted after methylene blue staining, removed and the remaining mucosae were coiled into "Swiss rolls". Muc5ac expression was studied by immunohistology using an anti-Muc5ac Mab (Mab 660).
Results: The number of ACF increased during first five months but decreased by the 15th month (except for large ACF). During the first month, the mucosae showed large numbers of Muc5ac positive dysplastic glands. The number of these glands decreased after the first month. Some histologically normal isolated glands expressed Muc5ac mucin but their number also decreased during carcinogenesis after the 2nd month. At the site of MNNG deposition, a large (1cm) agglomeration of lymphoid cells was observed as early as the 2nd week, showing adjacent dysplasic glands stained by Mab 660. At this level, at the 15th month, 50% of the rats developed adenomas which were strongly stained with the Mab 660. A diet containing 2% URSO did not cause any immunohistochemical differences during carcinogenesis.
Conclusions: Our results show that the expression of gastric Muc5ac mucin is an early event which takes place during colon carcinogenesis.

P-50 Gastrointestinal Ca.

Diagnostic value of logistic regression and tumour markers in pancreatic cancer

Louhimo Johanna[1], Alfthan H[2], Stenman U-H[2], Haglund C[1]
[1]Department of Surgery, [2] Clinical Chemistry, University of Helsinki, Finland

Aims: The diagnostic value of combined use of serum tumour markers CEA, CA19-9, CA242, CA72-4 and hCGβ was evaluated in pancreatic cancer.
Methods: Pancreatic cancer group (n=160, 79 males) consisted of 10 patients with stage I, 25 with stage II, 24 with stage III, and 101 with stage IV cancer. The control group (n=79, 50 males) comprised patients with pancreatitis or with jaundice due to benign conditions. The diagnostic value of various marker combinations was evaluated with logistic regression (LR) analysis.
Results: The respective sensitivities and specificities of the tumour markers were: 46% and 86% for CEA, 87% and 78% for CA19-9, 68% and 94% for CA242, 39% and 99% for CA72-4, and 63% and 90% for hCGβ. With receiver operating characteristic (ROC) curve analysis, CA19-9 and CA242 had the highest accuracies (area under the curve (AUC) values 0.861 and 0.857). Including the five tumour markers simultaneously in the LR model, serum CEA, CA19-9, CA72-4 and hCG β provided significant diagnostic information ($p<0.008$), indicating that their combination improves accuracy The probability of cancer –index, calculated from the LR algorithm with the combination of CEA, CA19-9, CA72-4 and hCGβ, provided significantly higher accuracy with ROC-curve analysis than CA19-9 (AUC 0.931; $p= 0.014$).
Conclusions: In pancreatic cancer, diagnostic accuracy may be improved by combining several tumour markers with LR analysis.

P-51 Gastrointestinal Ca.

Clinical utility of the ARCHITECT® CA 19-9™$_{XR}$ assay

O'Morchoe S[1], Covert B[2], Smith G[2], Kula K[1], Olson J[1], Rosiere Thomas[1]
[1]Abbott Diagnostics Division, Abbott Park, IL; [2]Fujirebio Diagnostics Inc, Malvern, PA, USA

Aims: The clinical utility of the ARCHITECT CA 19-9$_{XR}$ assay as an aid for pancreatic cancer patient management was assessed and compared to three currently marketed CA 19-9 assays.
Methods: The ARCHITECT CA 19-9$_{XR}$ assay is for quantitative determination of 1116-NS-19-9 reactive determinants using a two-step, chemiluminescent paramagnetic microparticle immunoassay format. Samples from patients with known malignant and non-malignant conditions were tested and compared to CA 19-9 RIA, AxSYM® CA 19-9™ and ARCHITECT® CA 19-9™ assay results.
Results: In a mixed population of 703 malignant and non-malignant samples, concordance to 37 U/mL versus CA 19-9 RIA, AxSYM CA 19-9 and ARCHITECT CA 19-9 was 92-94%. Of the discordant samples with CA 19-9$_{XR}$ values < 37 U/mL, 77-94% were nonmalignant; in those with values > 37 U/mL, 75-85% were malignant. The effectiveness to monitor disease status was determined by assessing concentration changes in serial samples from 74 pancreatic cancer patients compared to changes in disease status. With ARCHITECT CA 19-9$_{XR}$, the overall concordance to disease state was found to be 63% and 69% on sequential pair and per patient bases. Testing the same samples with the gold standard CA 19-9 RIA assay gave concordance to disease values of 63% and 65%.
Conclusions: The ARCHITECT CA 19-9$_{XR}$ has enhanced clinical specificity and is an effective aid for monitoring pancreatic cancer.

P-52 Gastrointestinal Ca.

Serum levels of EGFR, HER2 and VEGF in colorectal cancer

Spindler Karen-Lise Garm, Olsen DA, Jakobsen A, Brandslund I
Colorectal Cancer Group South, Department of Oncology, Laboratory Centre, Vejle Hospital, University of Southern Denmark, DK.

New treatment modalities targeting the epidermal growth factor receptor (EGFR) have been developed. EGFR testing by immunohistochemistry does not provide a basis for clinical decision making in EGFR targeted therapies. We are investigating alternate methods for testing the receptor status in colorectal cancer patients, among these serum values of EGFR.
Aims: To quantify serum protein levels of EGFR in patients with colorectal cancer and to correlate this to serum levels of HER2 and VEGF.
Methods: 79 serum samples from colorectal cancer patients were collected preoperatively. Serum-EGFR was evaluated by ELISA kit (Oncogene Science, USA), serum-HER2 by chemiluminescense assay for Advia Centauer (Bayer, USA), and serum-VEGF by ELISA kit (R&D systems, USA).
Results: The mean serum level of EGFR (33.6ng/ml) and HER2 (5.95ng/ml) was lower than that of the control groups (57.4ng/ml / 9.4ng/ml). P<0.000000. (Two-sample T-test). We found a correlation between EGFR and HER2–serum levels (R^2= 0,3859). Serum VEGF-levels in colorectal cancer patients were not significantly different from the control group and did not correlate to EGFR or HER2.
Conclusions: There is limited literature concerning coexpression of S-EGFR and S-HER2 in colorectal cancer. Our findings of decreased serum levels indicate a combined systemic mechanism within the epidermal growth factor receptor system. Serum measurement of EGFR and HER2 needs further evaluation as tools in clinical settings.

P-53 Gastrointestinal Ca.

Prognosis in 1089 non-metastatic colorectal cancer patients: Multivariate evaluation of preoperative levels of CEA and CA 19-9 in addition to clinical parameters

Hofmann Dominik, Stieber P, Lau-Werner U[1], Nagel D, Seidel D,
Institute of Clinical Chemistry, [1]Department of Surgery, University of Munich, Germany

Aims: For CEA and CA 19-9 prognostic relevance in colorectal cancer has been described. Currently, it is still unclear which of these markers are able to provide additive information to established prognostic factors in non-metastatic colorectal cancer.
Methods: We investigated for both tumor markers (CEA, Abbott, AxSYM; CA 19-9:Roche, Elecsys) whether they have additive prognostic value to tumor stage in 1089 patients with non-metastatic colorectal cancer.
Results: For evaluating disease free survival (DFS) and overall tumor-related survival (OTS), based on recommendations for adjuvant treatment, patients were divided into the good prognosis group (GPG: colon cancer stage I-II or rectal cancer stage I) and the bad prognosis group (BPG) consisting of the remaining patients with indication for adjuvant treatment.
Evaluating tumor markers, linearity was tested. In case of non-linearity a cut-off value was determined. Log (CEA) showed linearity in the GPG and BPG. In the GPG CEA was the only significant tumor marker, whereas in the BPG CEA and CA 19-9 were significant predictors.
In multivariate Cox regression analysis T stage ($p<0.001$) and CEA ($p=0.049$) proved independent relevance in the GPG, whereas T stage ($p<0.001$), N stage ($p<0.001$) and CA 19-9 (cut-off 55 U/ml; $p=0.018$) were independent predictors in the BPG.
Conclusions: Due to the resulting overlap of the prognosis groups, CEA and possibly CA 19-9 in addition to tumor stage and site should be considered for decisions on adjuvant treatment.

P-54 Lung Ca.

The prognostic significance of serum chromogranin A (CGA), progastrin releasing peptide (ProGRP) and neuron-specific enolase (NSE) in patients with advanced NSCLC

Nisman Benjamin, Heshing N, Biran H, Barak V, Peretz T
Oncology Department, Hadassah University Hospital, Jerusalem, and Sheibe Institute of Oncology, Kaplan Hospital, Rehovot, Israel

Aims: CGA, ProGRP and NSE are known as immunohistochemical markers, closely associated with neuroendocrine differentiation in NSCLC. The aim of the present study was to assess the value of serum levels of these markers in predicting survival of patients with advanced non-small cell lung cancer (NSCLC).
Methods: The study included 67 NSCLC patients, all of whom had received chemotherapy. Pretreatment CGA, ProGRP and NSE serum levels were measured with commercial kits.
Results: Our results show that three serum neuroendocrine markers contribute differently to prognosis. While NSE had no impact on prognosis, the median survival was found to be shorter for patients with elevated serum CGA and longer for patients with high ProGRP levels. On inclusion in multivariate Cox models both CGA and ProGRP retained significance with an opposite effect on survival (CGA, RR–1.8; P=0.04 and ProGRP, RR–0.5; P=0.03). The combined use of CGA, ProGRP and NSE allowed the definition of 2 sets of patients with significantly different median survival times (25.2 months vs. 8.8 months, P=0.001).
Conclusions: CGA and ProGRP in circulation appear to bear important prognostic information in NSCLC before chemotherapy. While a high CGA was found as an unfavourable prognostic determinant, a high ProGRP conferred a survival advantage. The combined use of all three neuroendocrine markers may provide an additional predictive capacity.

P-55 Lung Ca.

Is CYFRA 21-1 and CEA estimation helpful in preoperative assessment of non-small cell lung cancer (NSCLC) patients?

Szturmowicz Monika, Rudzi ski P, Kacprzak A, Langfort R, Demkow U, Bestry I, Orłowski T
National Institute of Tuberculosis and Lung Diseases, Warsaw, Poland

Aims: A pilot study designed to assess the role of CEA and CYFRA 21-1 estimation before surgical treatment and one week after the operation in NSCLC patients (pts).
Methods: 43 NSCLC pts clinical stage I and II, 32 men, 11 women, median age 64 years, range 42-81 years entered the study. Adenocarcinoma (AD) was recognized in 22 pts, squamous cell lung cancer (SCC) in 17, other types (mixed, large) in 4. Pathologic stage of disease was Ia in 9 pts, Ib in 19, IIb in 8, IIIa in 4, IIIb in 2, IV (metastases in homolateral lung) in 1. Serum tumor markers were measured with Elecsys Roche before surgery and on day 5-7 after surgery.
Results: Preoperative CEA > 3.4 ng/ml was found in 16/43 pts (37%), 55% of AD and 12% of SCC. CEA> 5 ng/ml was found exclusively in AD. Preoperative CYFRA 21-1> 3.3 ng/ml was found in 14/43 pts (33%), 41% of SCC and 23% of AD. In SCC preoperative CYFRA 21-1 was significantly higher in pathologic T2 than in T1 tumours . Postoperative serum CYFRA 21-1 normalized in all of the patients, CEA remained elevated in 8 pts.
Conclusions: CYFRA 21-1 and CEA estimation before surgical treatment and in early postoperative period of time may help to predict pathologic stage of disease in NSCLC and possibly indicate the pts in whom the treatment was not radical.

P-56 Lung Ca.

Development of a sandwich EIA for determination of proGRP 31-98

Öhrvik A, Dahlén U, Persson I., Fermér C, Olle Nilsson
CanAg Diagnostics AB, Gothenburg, Sweden

Aims: ProGRP (Pro Gastrin Releasing Peptide) is a stable precursor of the gut hormone gastrin releasing peptide (GRP). This marker of small cell lung cancer (SCLC) is more organ and tumor specific than other markers of relevance for lung cancer. We here describe the development of a sensitive assay for serum proGRP (31-98).
Methods: Monoclonal antibodies were developed from mice immunized with recombinant proGRP peptide 31-98. Mab E146 reactive against proGRP aa 48-53 was fragmented to $F(ab')_2$ and biotinylated. Mab E168 reactive against proGRP aa 83-88 was conjugated to horseradish peroxidase. The assay is a one-step sandwich EIA performed in microtiter wells coated with streptavidin using recombinant proGRP (31-98) calibrator.
Results: The analytical sensitivity is below 2 ng/L and the measuring range covers 5 – 1000 ng/L. Inter and intra assay % cv is < 5%. Linearity on dilutions ranges from 90-110%. No high dose hook was noticed up to 200 000 ng/L. Heterophilic antibodies did not interfere in the assay. The estimated upper 95th percentile in healthy individuals was < 30 ng/L. A study comparing proGRP EIA and proGRP ELISA (Advanced Life Sciences Inc.) demonstrated a high correlation between the methods. (r=0.98)
Conclusions: CanAg proGRP EIA is precise, sensitive and appears to be resistant to interference. It may provide a practical tool in the management of SCLC patients.

P-57 Lung Ca.

Prognostic value of SCCA2 isoform in NSCLC patients

Kulpa Jan[1], Wójcik E[1], Kami ska J[2], Einarsson R[3], Kowalska M[2], Migas B[1]
Center of Oncology – M.Skłodowska-Curie Memorial Institute, [1]Cracow and [2]Warsaw Divisions, Poland, [3]CanAg AB, Sweden

Aim: The utility of SCC antigen as a prognostic factor in NSCLC is controversial. There were observed differences between normal and malignant tissues in expressions of SCC isoforms. SCCA2 is predominantly expressed in cancer tissue. The aim of the study was to assess the prognostic value of serum SCC-Ag and its isoforms, CYFRA 21-1 levels, as well as of specific proteins in NSCLC.
Methods: Determinations of SCC-Ag, SCCA1, SCCA2, CYFRA 21-1, CRP, AAG and prealbumin were performed before treatment in 117 NSCLC patients. For all patients Cancer Serum Index (CSI) was calculated.
Results: NSCLC patients showed significantly higher concentrations of acute phase proteins, tumor markers, and CSI values than the reference group. SCCA1/SCCA2 ratio was higher in NSCLC than in the reference group. Patients not qualified to surgery had significantly higher CRP, AAG, CYFRA 21-1, SCC-Ag, SCCA1 levels, and CSI values than those at earlier stages of disease. SCCA1/SCCA2 ratio in NSCLC patients with [I+II+IIIA] stages was significantly lower in comparison to patients with [IIIB+IV]. Univariate analysis confirmed that. stage of disease, CYFRA 21-1, SCC-Ag, SCCA1, SCCA2, CRP and CSI appeared to influence survival of NSCLC patients. Multivariate analysis revealed that stage of disease, CSI and SCCA2 were independent prognostic factors in NSCLC patients.
Conclusions: SCCA2 and CSI may contribute additional information for evaluation of NSCLC patients' prognosis.

P-58 Lung Ca.

Prognostic factors in small cell lung cancer

Wójcik Ewa, Kulpa J, Dymek P, Stasik Z, Sas-Korczy ska B
Center of Oncology – M.Sklodowska-Curie Memorial Institute, Cracow Division, Poland

Aim: The aim of the study was to assess the utility of some tumor markers, interleukins and acute phase proteins for the evaluation of survival in small cell lung cancer patients.
Methods: The determination of albumin, prealbumin, alpha-1 acid-glycoprotein, C-reactive protein, interleukin 6, CYFRA 21-1, NSE, ProGRP and LDH were performed in a group of 83 small cell lung cancer patients. Cancer Serum Index (CSI) and Nutritional Risk Index (NRI) were also calculated for each patient.
Results: Apart from dependencies between tumor markers (NSE vs. ProgRP: $r = 0.4343$, NSE vs. LDH: $r = 0.6533$) the group of SCLC patients presented a positive correlation between CRP vs. IL-6, and CSI , and a reciprocal correlation between CRP and NRI. Patients with CRP above 10 mg/L, in comparison to those with CRP below this value, were characterized by significantly higher NSE concentrations and LDH activity, and a lack of differences between both groups for ProGRP and CYFRA 21-1 levels. Univariate analysis revealed that PS<80%, age<58 years, NRI<90.5, CSI>7.0, CRP>25.0 mg/L, IL-6>6.0 pg/mL, CYFRA 21-1>3.8 ng/ml, NSE > 46.5 ng/ml, ProGRP>510 ng/ml, LDH>450 U/l, had a significant impact on 2- year survival. In SCLC patients independent prognostic factors were, besides the extent of disease, CRP, CYFRA 21-1 and ProGRP.
Conclusions: ProGRP, CYFRA 21-1, CRP seem to provide information in addition to stage of disease for the evaluation of SCLC patients prognosis.

P-59 Lung Ca.

Evaluation of six serum tumour markers in patients with lung adenocarcinoma

Vaslamatzis MM[1], Kyriou L[2], Vrionis E[1], Stathopoulos Ch[1], Petraki C[3], Moustafellou A[2], et al.
Depts of: [1]Medical Oncology, [2]Biochemistry, [3]Pathology, Evangelismos Hospital, Athens, Greece

Aims: To prospectively evaluate the incidence & prognostic impact of serum CEA, NSE, CA-125, SCC, TPS & Cyfra21.1 in 77 patients(pts) with lung adenocarcinoma before & after treatment.
Methods: We evaluated 60(78%) men & 17(22%) women, median age 59y (40-78), consecutively admitted to our unit between 6/99-4/05. Stage IIIa had 23(30%) & IIIb+IV 54(70%) patients.
Results: Elevated serum CEA, NSE, CA-125, SCC, TPS & Cyfra21.1 before treatment were observed in 32(41.5%), 30(39%), 37(48%), 18(23%), 33(43%) & 35(45%) of patients, respectively. More than three increased serum markers were found in 22/77(28.5%) pts, 17/60(28%) men, 5/17(29%) women (p=NS), 20/54(37%) IIIb+IV vs 2/23(9%) stage IIIa (p=0.01). There was a strong correlation between the number of pts of stages IIIb+IVvsIIIa & high CEA (29/54vs3/23, p=0.001), NSE(25/54vs5/23, p=0.004), CA-125(31/54vs6/23, p=0.012), TPS(28/54vs5/23, p=0.015) & CYFRA21.1(30/54vs5/23, p=0.006). There was a significant association between the number of pts with >3 abnormal markers & stages IIIb+IV(20/54vs2/23, p=0.012). All pts received platinum based chemotherapy, 66(86%) completed at least 3 cycles & were re-evaluated. Overall response(OR) was documented in 25(38%) of them. Only increased pretherapeutic serum NSE was correlated with worse OR (3/28vs22/38, p<0.001.)
Conclusions: In our pts: 1. CA-125, Cyfra21.1 & TPS, had the highest sensitivity. 2. A strong correlation between increased values of CEA, NSE, CA-125, TPS & Cyfra21.1 & stages IIIb+IV was observed. 3. About 28.5% of pts IIIb+IV had at least 4 elevated markers before treatment. 4. Pretherapeutically elevated serum NSE seemed to have predictive usefulness for the outcome.

P-60 Lung Ca.

Nucleosomes predict early the response to chemotherapy in lung cancer patients

Holdenrieder Stefan[1], Stieber P[1], von Pawel J[2], Raith H[2], Nagel D[1], Feldmann K[2], Seidel D[1]
[1]University Hospital Munich-Grosshadern, Munich; [2]Asklepios Hospital, Gauting, Germany

Background: Facing an era of new antitumor therapies, predictors of therapy response are needed for the individual management of the treatment.
Methods: In prospectively collected sera of 472 patients with advanced NSCLC (311 first-line and 161 second-line chemotherapy), the courses of nucleosomes, CYFRA 21-1, CEA, NSE, ProGRP, M30 and caspases were investigated and correlated with the later therapy response.
Results: In patients with first-line chemotherapy, those with remission showed significantly (p<0.05) lower values of nucleosomes and CYFRA 21-1 for the pretherapeutic baseline values of cylce 1, 2, 3 (BV1, BV2, BV3), for the area under the curve of days 1-8 (AUC1-8) and for day 8 of first cycle than patients with progression. Additionally CEA (BV3, BV1-2, BV1-3), NSE (BV2), and M30 (BV3) discriminated between both groups. Among them, nucleosomes (day8) and CYFRA 21-1 (BV2) exhibited the best profile of positive predictive value and sensitivity for progression. Both markers were independent from each other, from stage and performance score. In combination, they predicted progression with a specificity of 100% in 29% of the cases.
In patients receiving second-line chemotherapy, the same combination enabled the early prediction of progression at 100%-specificity in 19% of the cases.
Conclusion: Nucleosomes and CYFRA 21-1 identify a subgroup of NSCLC-patients with insufficient therapy response already at the early treatment phase.

P-61 Lung Ca.

Serum MMP-9 and TIMP-1 values in lung cancer

Oguz Soydinc Hilal, Duran Yildiz D, Dalay N, Camlica H, Kaytan Saglam E, Yasasever V
University of Istanbul, Institute of Oncology, Istanbul-Turkey

Aims: Lung cancer is the most frequent cause of death among malignant diseases. Radiotherapy (RT) is an important treatment modality in lung cancer, especially for inoperable patients. Degradation of the extracellular matrix (ECM) is an essential step in cancer invasion and metastasis. Matrix metalloproteinases (MMPs) are capable of degrading ECM components. Detection of high levels of MMPs in cancer may provide useful markers for predicting metastases. The present study was conducted to investigate the value of serum MMP-9 and TIMP-1 levels and to determine the effects of radiotherapy on these parameters in lung cancer patients.
Methods: We investigated the serum MMP-9 and TIMP-1 values in 20 lung cancer patients before RT, on day 14th. and after completion of RT by ELISA. The results were compared with the controls (n=20).
Results: Statistical significance was determined with the Student's t test. Before RT, MMP-9 (t= 2,95) and TIMP-1 (t= 3,1) values were significantly higher than the controls (p< 0,001). RT was followed by a statistically non-significant decrease in serum MMP-9 values but not in TIMP-1.
Conclusions: The decrease of MMP-9 after the initiation of RT was possibly caused by the suppressive effect of radiation.

P-62 Lung Ca.

Prognostic relevance of nucleosomes, S100-protein, neuron-specific enolase, and c-reactive protein in patients with acute cerebral stroke

Geiger Sandra[1], Holdenrieder S[1], Stieber P[1], Hamann GF[2], Bruening R[3], Ma J[3], Nagel D[1], Seidel D[1]
[1]Institute of Clinical Chemistry, [2]Department of Neurology, [3]Department of Neuroradiology, University Hospital Munich-Grosshadern, Munich, Germany

Background: Several specific and non-specific markers were investiga-ted on their prognostic relevance for the later recovery in stroke patients.
Patients and Methods: In sera of 63 patients with acute cerebral stroke, nucleosomes, NSE, S100, CRP and leukocytes were determined daily during the first week after the ischemic event. Additionally, infarction volume and clinical status (by Barthel Index=BI) at admission, discharge, and after 12 months (prognosis) were assessed.
Results: Infarction volume, nucleosomes (days3,6), NSE (days3,6), S100 (days3,6), CRP (day3), and leukocytes (day3) correlated significantly (p<0.05) with clinical status (BI) at admission. Concerning prognosis, initial BI, infarction volume, nucleosomes (days3,6), NSE (days3,6), and S100 (days3,6) correlated with the later outcome, but not CRP and leukocytes. Almost all patients with initial BI≥50 reached complete recovery. In patients with initially severe defects (BI<50), nucleosomes (day3), and S100 protein (day3) were found to be still prognostically relevant. At 100%-specificity for non-recovery, only nucleosomes (day3) maintained their prognostic power (sensitivity 38%; p=0.014), whereas S100 (day3) did not (sensitivity 16.7%; p=0.25). In multivariate analysis, nucleosomes and BI at admission showed independent prognostic relevance (p=0.039).
Conclusion: Circulating nucleosomes and clinical scores provide independent prognostic information concerning the later outcome in patients with initially severe defects after stroke.

Multiparametric analysis of prognosis in patients with small cell lung cancer

Holdenrieder Stefan[1], von Pawel J[2], Raith H[2], Feldmann K[2], Stenman UH[3], Nagel D[1], Stieber P[1]
[1]University Hospital Munich-Grosshadern, Munich, Germany;
[2]Asklepios Hospital, Gauting, Germany;
[3]Helsinki University Central Hospital, Helsinki, Finland

Background: Currently available data concerning the prognostic relevance of biochemical markers in SCLC are conflicting.
Methods: In a prospective study on 121 patients with newly diagnosed SCLC undergoing chemotherapy, we investigated 56 pretherapeutic parameters including 19 clinical factors, 22 "classical" laboratory markers and 15 oncological biomarkers. First, clinical parameters with independent prognostic relevance were selected by Cox-regression analysis. Second, all log-transformed values of biochemical markers were included separately in Cox-regression analyses with relevant clinical factors. Finally, all markers which remained in the models with $p<0.1$ were analyzed by Cox-regression using both forward and backward selection in parallel.
Results: Median observation time of all 121 patients was 6.6 months. In multivariate analysis of clinical factors, only performance score (PS) and weight loss (WL) showed prognostic relevance. In subsequent Cox-regression analyses including separately all biochemical markers with PS and WL, 11 were retained including LDH, albumin, NSE, CYFRA 21-1, CgA, TATI, calcium, urea, AST, GGT, and platelets. When these markers were included in both forward and backward selection, the resulting multivariate model comprised PS, WL, ln-albumin, and ln-LDH.
Conclusion: Standardized procedure for establishing prognosis in SCLC revealed PS, WL, albumin and LDH as independent prognostic markers.

P-64 Tumor Biology

Comparative analysis of human and mouse genomes identified vitamin D receptor as a direct target of p53-mediated transcriptional activation

Maruyama Reo, Toyota M, Shinomura Y, Tokino T, Imai K
First Dept. of Internal Medicine, Sapporo Medical University, Sapporo, Japan

Aims: Identification of target genes of p53 is important to understand the role of p53 in variety of biological functions. We have tried to predict novel p53 target genes by computational approach.
Methods: To identify novel p53 target genes, we performed in comparative analysis of human and mouse genome. After multiple filtering procedures, sixty genes were identified as putative p53 target genes. Among these genes, we examined vitamin D receptor (VDR) gene in detail because vitamin D3 is recently used as in chemoprevention of human tumors.
Results: VDR expression was induced by p53 and p53 family genes in variety cancer cell lines. ChIP assays showed that candidate p53-binding sequences located in the VDR first intron could directly interact with the p53 protein in vivo, and Luciferase assays confirmed the p53-response sequence was functional. Overexpression of VDR increased the sensitivity to vitamin D3 treatment, and suppressed colony growth of colorectal cancer cells. Furthermore we observed several p53 target genes were up-regulated by vitamin D3 treatment under VDR overexpression condition.
Conclusions: these results demonstrate that the VDR is a target for transcriptional activation by p53 and suggest that p53 might sensitize cells to the anti-proliferative actions of vitamin D3 by increasing VDR levels.

P-65 Tumor Biology

Recombinant third domain of human alpha-fetoprotein: selectivity and antitumor activity of conjugate with Taxol.

Savvateeva Lyudmila, Gorokhovets N [1], Makarov V [1], Posypanova G, Severin S
Moscow Research Institute of Medical Ecology, Moscow, Russia,
[1] Moscow I.M. Sechenov Medical Academy

Aims: To study selectivity and cytotoxicity of recombinant third domain of human alpha-fetoprotein (rhAFP3D) conjugate with Taxol against tumor cells *in vitro.*
Methods: cDNA of rhAFP3D was cloned into the pET-28 vector and expressed in *E.coli* strain BL21(DE3). The rhAFP3D was purified by metalo-chelating and gel-permeating chromatography. The rhAFP3D conjugate with Taxol was synthesized, the rhAFP3D:Taxol molar ratio was 1:1.5. The biological activity of the rhAFP3D-Taxol complex was tested with the human tumor cell lines: MCF-7, DU145, SKOV3. The survival rate of cells was evaluated using the MTT-test.
Results: The rhAFP3D has been shown to avidly bind and selectively enter tumor cell (in contrast to unstimulated lymphocytes) via receptor-mediated endocytotic pathway. The cytotoxic activity of rhAFP3D-Taxol conjugate against the cell lines tested appeared to be comparable to that of natural AFP-Taxol conjugate. The data obtained testify that the rhAFP3D can be used instead of natural AFP, which requires complicated isolation procedure.
Conclusions: The application of rhAFP3D as a vector for targeted delivery of chemotherapeutic drug makes it possible to enhance the selective toxicity of the conjugate against human tumor cells. The high efficiency of the antitumor effect of rhAFP3D-Taxol suggests that the synthetic rhAFP3D-Taxol conjugate is a promising chemotherapeutic agent.

P-66 Tumor Biology

The human prothrombin kringle-2 derived peptide, NSA9, is internalized into bovine capillary endothelial cells through endocytosis and energy-dependent pathways

Hyun Sook Hwang, Kim TH, and Kim SS
Department of Biochemistry, College of Science, Yonsei University, Korea

Aims: Human prothrombin kringle-2 and its partial peptide, NSA9 (NSAVQLVEN), have been reported to have potent anti-angiogenic activities in BCE cell proliferation, CAM angiogenesis assay and mouse tumor model. In the present studies, we examined the internalization mechanism of the potent anti-angiogenic NSA9 peptide into BCE cells.
Methods: We synthesized FITC-labeled NSA9 and investigated the internalization of NSA9 for the time dependence, its effect on cellular membrane, and relation to endocytosis pathway using lactate dehydrogenase release assay, fluorescence microscopy, and flow cytometry.
Results: NSA9 was internalized by BCE cells in a time dependent manner for 6 h of incubation without affecting cellular membrane integrity and the internalized NSA9 showed a punctuated fluorescence pattern, which is indicative of endocytic vesicles. The intracellular localization of NSA9 was significantly inhibited by some endocytosis and metabolic inhibitors and low temperature. Also, when cellular uptake of NSA9 was blocked by endocytosis or metabolic inhibitors, NSA9 failed to inhibit the proliferation of BCE cells.
Conclusions: These results suggest that the human prothrombin kringle-2 derived peptide, NSA9, is internalized into BCE cells through endocytosis and energy-dependent pathways and then exerts its anti-proliferative activity against BCE cells.

P-67 Tumor Biology

Apoptotic tumor suppression effect of anti- erbB2 chimeric monoclonal antibody

Masayuki*, Tsujisaki Y**, Kato T**, Matsune S***, Sasaki K***, Imai K***
*)1st Dept. of Clinical Medicine, Tenshi Hospital, Caress Alliance Medical Corporation , Sapporo, Japan. **) Sapporo Shirakabadai Hospital, Sapporo, Japan. ***)1st Dept. of Internal Medicine, Sapporo Medical University, Sapporo, Japan

Aims: It is known that the human erbB-2 oncogene encodes a 185 kDa glycoprotein with a tyrosin kinase activity and erbB-2 protein is necessary for the malignant transformation. This protein is often overexpressed and amplified in breast, ovarian and gastric cancers. ErbB-2 gene product is one of the best target molecules for cancer therapy. We established an anti-erbB-2 mouse human chimeric monoclonal antibody (MoAb) CH401, which was able to kill erbB-2 positive cancer cells in vitro and suppress tumor grouth in vivo.
We studied its therapeutic usefulness and the mechanism of growth suppression.
Methods and Results: The study of the killing mechanism clarified that chimeric MoAb CH401 could induce the apoptosis of cancer cells. The effects of CH401 to MAPK cascade were investigated in order to study the apoptosis mechanism induced by MoAb CH401.
In conclusion, MoAb CH401 activates the JNK and p38 MAP kinase pathway and the ERK pathway, resulting in apoptosis, not in growth. Furthermore, the difference between Trastuzumab and MoAb CH401 was investigated.
Conclusions: Trastuzumab non-regulates the ERK, JNK and p38 pathway in erbB-2 transfected SV22 cells and does not induce apoptosis.

P-68 Tumor Biology

Charge dependence of cellular uptake and selective anti-tumor activity of porphyrazines

Vesper Benjamin J[1], Hammer ND[1], Lee S[2], Elseth K[1], Hoffman BM[2], Radosevich JA[1]
[1]Center for Molecular Biology of Oral Diseases, College of Dentistry, University of Illinois-Chicago, Chicago, IL, USA, [2]Dept. of Chemistry, Northwestern University, Evanston, IL, USA

Aims: The porphyrazines (pzs) are a class of porphyrin derivatives possessing distinctive chemical and physical features, making them excellent candidates as optical imaging/therapeutic agents. The novelty of the pzs requires that we first determine how specific structures selectively alter biological function. In the first of these studies, we here present a correlation of pz charge with biocompatibility.
Methods: Three peripherally functionalized $H_2A_2B_2$ (*trans* conformation) pzs, where A is $[S\text{-}R]_2$ and B is a fused diisopropyloxybenzo ring, were synthesized. Each possessed a different R group, resulting in a different charge: neutral, R = $(CH_2CH_2O)_3H$ (16^0); positive, R = $(CH_2)_2O(CH_2)_2Py^+$ (42^+); and negative, R = $(CH_2)_3CO_2^-$ (18^-). Pz-treated A549 tumor cells (TC) and WI-38 VA13 normal cells (NC) were monitored for cellular uptake and localization via fluorescence microscopy, and MTT assays were used to measure concentration/time/light-dependent proliferation/viability.
Results: The three pzs differ in their toxicity, uptake, and localization in the two different cell lines. Interestingly, 18^- was found to exhibit selective dark toxicity in TC at a treatment concentration of 25 M.
Conclusions: Pz functional groups can be easily modified and, as shown here, can result in specific structure-function relationships, suggesting these compounds as a class offer substantial promise as biomedical agents.

P-69 Tumor Biology

Porphyrazine structure-function relationships: effect of core metal and number of peripheral acid groups on biological behavior

Vesper Benjamin J[1], Hammer ND[1], Lee S[2], Elseth K[1], Hoffman BM[2], Radosevich JA[1]
[1]University of Illinois-Chicago, College of Dentistry, Center of Molecular Biology of Oral Diseases, Chicago, IL, USA, [2]Northwestern University, Dept. of Chemistry, Evanston, IL, USA

Aims: The porphyrazines (pzs) are a family of porphyrin derivatives recently being investigated for their anti-tumor applications due to their superior optical properties and ease of synthesis. We here begin to determine how specific structures alter the biological function of pzs, leading to "rules" that will predict biologically active pzs.
Methods: A family of peripherally functionalized $M[pz(A_n;B_{4-n})]$ pzs with n = 4, 3, or 2 (in a *trans* conformation), where A is $[S(CH_2)_3COOH]$, B is a fused -diisopropyloxybenzo ring, and M=H_2, Zn, or Co were synthesized. The viability of pz-treated tumor cells (TCs) and normal cells (NCs) were assessed using MTT assays.
Results: Cellular toxicity after prolonged exposure to the free-base pzs was found to increase with increasing number of pz acid moieties, and for each compound studied, the percentage of TCs killed was greater than the percentage of NCs killed. The metallated pzs were significantly less toxic to both TCs and NCs.
Conclusions: The number of acid functionalities on a given pz, as well as the core metal of the pz, has a direct impact on cellular toxicity, thereby identifying an important structure-function relationship that can be utilized when preparing future compounds.

P-70 Tumor Biology

Electromagnetic (EMG) signals of nerve growth factor (NGF) may induce differentiation of rat pheochromatocytoma cells PC 12

Karkabounas Spiros C[1], Scarpelis G[1], Havelas K[1], Metsios A[1], Hadjiavazis G[1], Giotis C[2], Evangelou AM[1]
[1]Lab of Physiology, Medical School, University of Ioannina; [2]Nephrolgy Clinic, General Hospital of Arta, Greece

Aims: In this study we investigated whether EMG signals may induce differentiation of PC12 cells.
Methods: The NGF EMG signals were recorded by a device emitting EMG waves and recording the resonance to the waves emitted by the substance tested. Emission of NGF signals was performed by *Multi Channel Dynamic Exciter 100 VI* utilizing an EMF generator of RW, at various intensities. The PC12 cells were cultured for 10 days and then in a Faraday cage: 1.Experimental sample (ExS) cells were exposed to static EMF signals of NGF, for 12 hours a day for 3 consecutive days, 2. Control sample (CS) cells were exposed with the device switched off, for the same period of time. Comparison samples (COS) of cells were cultured in presence of human NGF at various concentrations (1to20 μg/ml).
Results: A band of frequencies between 10 kHz to 200 kHz, was recorded for NGF. CS cells showed a slight increase in proliferation rate with no morphological changes at the end of the experiment. COS cells showed a dose dependent increase of its proliferation rate and differentiation in nervous cells. ExS cells showed no significant increase of proliferation rate after the exposure to the signals of NGF. After the end of 3rd exposure a high percentage (>50 %) of PC12 cells presented morphological features of nervous cells and a formation of neuronal networks. Repeated cultures of the EMF exposed cells revealed that they conserve their differentiation features for long, while, if no NGF is added in the culture media of the comparison samples, cells abolish their differentiation within 3 days.
Conclusions: NGF as other substances[1] emit signals of EMG nature that, if transmitted to target cells (PC12), may cause their differentiation to nervous cells, similar and more permanent to that the substance itself can do.

P-71 Tumor Biology

Somatic mutations and activation-induced cytidine deaminase (AID) expression in a rheumatoid factor producing lymphoblastoid cell line

Yaniv Gill, Levy, S, Steinitz, M and Laskov, R
The Hebrew Univ-Hadassah Medical School, Jerusalem, Israel

Aims: The question whether Epstein-Bar virus (EBV) transformed lymphoblastoid cell lines (LCLs) exhibit somatic mutations in their Ig variable region genes (IgV) during in vitro growth was studied.
Methods: The sequences of the rearranged V_H of an adult-LCL which secretes a monoclonal IgM rheumatoid factor (RF-line) and of the V •genes of cord blood LCLs were determined.
Results: EBV infection of adult and cord blood lymphocytes induces a rapid induction of AID, a mutator responsible for somatic hypermutation (SHM) in the IgV. SHM were not found in the rearranged V of cord blood LCLs. By contrast, the rearranged V_H gene of the RF-line, exhibited a low level of somatic mutations in culture. The mutations were preferentially targeted to the WRCH/DGYW hot spot motifs and biased for GC nucleotides, indicating that they were due to AID mediated SHM. Two point mutations in the CDR1&2 of the V_H of "non-antigen binding" RF clones, correlated with loss of antigen binding activity.
Conclusions: Induction AID expression and SHM in the rearranged V_H of adult-LCL, may explain the occasional loss of antigen binding activity occurring in freshly established antibody secreting LCLs. In addition, our results support the possibility that AID may act as an oncogene, since the tumorigenic outcome of EBV infection in B-cells, may be partly mediated by the induction of the mutatory activity of AID.

P-72 Standardization

The improper request of certain tumor markers through family physician in our A.S.O. reality

Viberti Giuseppina, Gonella S, Daglio C, Baldassi R, Bellati P
Department of Clinical Pathology, Ospedale S. Luigi Gonzaga, Orbassano (Torino), Abbott Diagnostics Division, Rome (Italy)

Aims: The purpose of this study was to evaluate the accuracy and correlation between a given clinical diagnosis and the tumor markers requested by the clinician.
Methods: Over 7300 patient prescriptions were verified throughout a single year and the tumor markers requested where compared against the diagnosis.
Results: Verification of prescription (out-patient / in-patient) and diagnoses indicated that 80% of the 799 prescriptions of AFP were correct; 41% of the 3989 prescriptions of PSA & FREE-PSA were correct; 34% of the 1713 prescriptions of CEA were correct; and 21% of the 850 prescriptions of Ca19.9 were correct. Our study also highlighted the existence of requests for combinations of tumor markers on the same prescription (35%).
Conclusions: Our analyses showed there was a need for better education and clearer guidelines on the use and prescription requests for tumor markers among family physicians.

P-73 Standardization

Questionable Results of NSE in EQA

Bartos Vladimir, Stern P, Uhrova J, Bezdickova D, Vanickova Z, Zima T, Safarcik K
Dept of Nuclear Medicine, University Hospital, Ostrava, Czech Republic

Aims: Evaluating NSE determinations in the Czech EQA system, differences between results acquired by some commonly used analytical systems were repeatedly observed. This makes us assume that some of the systems might give distorted results. We set our goal to find out the source of these discrepancies.
Methods: Two groups of samples - patient sera and controls - were analyzed by seven most frequently used systems (Elecsys –Roche, Kryptor – B.R.A.H.M.S., DELFIA – PerkinElmer, IRMA – Immunotech, CIS and DiaSorin, ELISA – DRG).
Results: The differences between the assessed systems were confirmed by the controls. ELISA DRG and Elecsys usually gave the lowest results. Such differences were not observed when patient samples were used. ELISA DRG kit gave the lowest results again, while Elecsys system corresponded with the others.
Conclusions: Most manufacturers of control materials admit differences between results, which depend on the method used (e.g. BioRef and BioRad producers declare values for IRMA CIS by 388% and 47% higher than for Elecsys). It is obvious that the results obtained by different immunoassays are considerably dependent on the matrix of samples. Different affinity of antibodies against - and - enolase isoenzymes in particular systems might be the cause of these discrepancies. The ratio of the isoenzymes is unlikely to be constant in the studied controls. This impact cannot be derived from the data provided by the manufacturer.

P-74 Standardization

Comparison of four methods for CA 19-9 determination

Sandri Maria Teresa[1], Passerini R[1], Bellati P[2], Chieregatti I[3], Dolci A[3]
[1]Laboratory Medicine Unit, European Institute of Oncology, Milan; [2]Abbott Diagnostics, Rome;
[3]Pathology Department, MultiMedica, Milan, Italy

Aims: CA 19-9 is frequently used in patients with adenocarcinomas of the pancreas and stomach, in gall bladder tumors and approximately in half of primary and metastatic ovarian tumors.
We compared the results of four analytical systems for CA 19-9 determination: Architect i 2000, AxSYM (Abbott Laboratories), Elecsys 1010 (Roche Diagnostics) and KRYPTOR (Brahms Diagnostics).
Methods: Eighty-one serum samples with CA 19-9 values covering the whole analytical range were tested. Statistical calculations were performed using Passing–Bablok regression and Bland Altman difference plot. The upper reference limit is 37 kU/L for AxSYM, Architect and Kryptor systems, 39 kU/L for Elecsys 1010.
Results: The Passing-Bablok correlation coefficients ranged from 0.9586 (Architect-Elecsys) to 0.9994 (AxSYM-Elecsys), the intercepts between 1.354 (AxSYM-Architect) and 12.097 (Architect-Kryptor) and the slopes from 0.6426 (Architect-Kryptor) to 1.1796 (AxSYM-Architect). Systematic differences evaluated by Bland Altman method were between 11.5 (AxSYM-Elecsys) and –88 (Kryptor-Architect).
Conclusions: Passing-Bablok regression show significant systemic difference between analytical systems, and Bland Altman plots significant individual differences among individual samples, mainly for high CA 19-9 concentrations. These results confirm that a standardization effort is mandatory, and that the patient follow-up must be performed keeping the method constant.

P-75 Standardization

CA15-3, CA125 and CA19-9 assay evaluation on Advia Centaur and Architect i2000SR

Bellati Paola[1], Montanelli A[2], Grassini A[2], Arsola L[2]
[1]Abbott Diagnostics, [2]Laboratory Analysis Crema Hospital Italy

Aims: We evaluated the performance of different system analyzers to determine mucin assay, necessary in order to provide consistent results to the clinicians for a better monitoring and management of patients in follow up.
Methods: We compared Advia Centaur (Bayer), already in use in our laboratory, with Architect i2000SR (Abbott). 230 fresh samples (53 CA 15-3, 60 CA 125 and 117 CA 19-9) were assayed in parallel on both analyzers to avoid preservation problems (freezing).
Results: For each data series were calculated regression and correlation coefficient, with the following results: CA15-3 showed $y = 0.982x + 0.65$ with $R^2 = 0.97$; CA 125 showed $y = 1.215x + 0.25$ with $R^2 = 0.98$ and CA 19-9 showed $y = 1.307x - 1.61$ with $R^2 = 0.75$.
These results showed remarkable correlation between CA15-3 and CA125. We encounter less correlation with CA19-9, probably due to a wide scattering of results. Five samples with discordant results (negative with Advia, pathological with Architect) highlighted the accuracy of Architect, reinforced with clinical study (four patients with gastrointestinal malignant disease, one with lymphoma).
Conclusions: In case of discrepancies, regarding CA 19-9, it's better to re-baseline the patient. Evidence of little overestimation of CA 125 Architect vs Advia, but nevertheless correlation and agreement between the two CA 125 and CA 15-3 methods where encouraging good.

P-76 Standardization

Site-specific immunization with phage displaying defined antigen epitopes

Fermér Christian, Majnesjö K, Röijer E, Andersson I, Nilsson O
CanAg Diagnostics AB, Gothenburg, Sweden

Aims: To evaluate the use filamentous phage displaying defined parts of antigens as immunogens in order to establish antibodies with pre-defined specificities. As test system Progastrin-releasing peptide (ProGRP) was used in order to generate site-specific antibodies in rabbits and mice. Furthermore the ProGRP specificity was rescued as single-chain Fv (scFv) antibodies.
Methods. Rabbits and mice were immunized with recombinant phage particles, constructed to display defined regions of ProGRP Serum samples were analysed for ProGRP titers in an ELISA assay. Antibody transcripts from B-cells of positive mice served as starting material for construction of a scFv library from which clones with specificity for ProGRP were selected.
Results: Serum samples from immunised rabbits demonstrated high reactivity to ProGRP. Sera from four out of six mice were positive, two with moderate and two with high titers towards ProGRP. Unique scFv clones with specificity for ProGRP were isolated from a phage library constructed from B-cells of mice with high anti ProGRP titers.
Conclusions: Earlier immunization schemes with recombinant ProGRP with or without carrier molecules (KLH, Ovalbumin) as well as with peptides have shown poor results. Therefore the results in the present study are especially encouraging indicating that "site-specific immunization" may be useful also for antigens that otherwise are difficult to raise antibodies against, and may also be a general method to raise high affinity reagents against specific regions of any protein.

P-77 Standardization

Lot-to-lot consistency of ARCHITECT® tumor marker assays: CA 125 II™, CA 15-3®, and SCC

Kula Kathleen[1], White K[2], Kobayashi Y[2], Kettlety T[3], Dickson G[3]
[1]Abbott Laboratories, Abbott Park, IL, [2]Abbott Laboratories, Tokyo, Japan; [3]Fujirebio Diagnostics Inc, Malvern, PA , USA

Aims: Consistent tumor marker reagent lot-to-lot performance over time is essential for patient management. Serial testing of patients for specific antigen levels in serum or plasma aids in determining response to therapy or for recurrence of disease. The ARCHITECT instrument system has demonstrated consistent reagent lot-to-lot performance using chemiluminescent microparticle immunoassay technology for CA 125 II, CA 15-3, and SCC* (*Only available outside of the US).
Methods: Quality control testing procedures report controls and serum panels at appropriate clinical levels for each ARCHITECT tumor marker assay. Data was collected over the last seven to thirteen months from all reagent lots manufactured for each assay since market availability.
Results: The control levels for each assay exhibited the following CVs: CA 125 II, ≤3.8%; CA 15-3, ≤3.2%; and SCC, ≤2.3%. For each assay, the serum panels at each level exhibited the following CVs: CA 125 II, ≤4.7%; CA 15-3, ≤5.6%; and SCC, ≤2.3%.
Conclusions: All three newly launched ARCHITECT tumor marker assays demonstrated consistent results between manufactured lots. Laboratorians and physicians can be confident that changes in the concentrations of tumor markers in patients' serum is indicative of changes in the patients' disease status and not a result of variability in assay manufacturing.

P-78 Standardization

Evaluation of reference intervals for six tumor markers in France

Pham P[1], Debuire B[1], Olson James[2]
[1]Department of Biochemistry, Paul Brousse Hospital, Villejuif, France; [2]Abbott Laboratories, Abbott Park, IL

Aims: The purpose of this study was to evaluate the range of values for tumor markers in specimens from normal subjects.
Methods: Apparently normal men and women were tested on the Abbott ARCHITECT® instrument using the following assays (and specimen numbers): CA 15-3 and CA 125 (149 women); total PSA (138 men); and AFP, CEA, and CA 19-9 (137 men and women).
Results: The following median values were obtained: AFP, 2.7 ng/mL; CEA, 1.6 µg/L; CA 19-9, 4 kU/L; CA 15-3, 13 kU/L; CA 125, 13.8 kU/L; total PSA, 0.59 µg/L. For CA 15-3 and CA 125, the sample population was divided into those less than 50 years old and those greater than or equal to 50 years of age. For CA 15-3, the under 50 median was 13.0 (mean 12.79); over 50 median was 13.1 (mean 13.24) kU/L. For CA 125, under 50 median was 13.6 (mean 15.13); over 50 median was 14.6 (mean 16.64) kU/L. For total PSA, the population was divided into the following: 20-39; 40-59; 60-79; and 80 years of age or greater. The total PSA median (and mean) for each group was: 0.48 (0.62); 0.50 (0.80); 0.85 (1.25); 1.29 (1.93) µg/L, respectively.
Conclusions: Median and mean values for these populations are comparable to published results and reflect the accuracy and precision of the assays tested.

P-79 Standardization

Changing the tumor markers platform-a challenge - CA 125 and CA 15-3 as an example

Barak M[1], Weiberger R[1], Olson James[2]
[1]Haifa and Western Galilee General Laboratory-Clalit Health Services Haifa, Israel;
[2]Abbott Diagnostics Division, Abbott Park, IL

Aims: Changing analyzers is a challenge in every laboratory and discipline but the implications when performing tumor markers are very significant in terms of treatment and perception of the malignant process – therefore for the last 8 years we haven't changed our platform for tumor markers-the Cobas Core® analyzer. Since Roche Diagnostics announced the upgrade of the tumor marker tests to other analyzers we were compelled to evaluate the performance of five different instruments-among them the ARCHITECT® system.
Methods: Our evaluation consisted of: 1. assays specifications comparisons paying attention especially to the measuring technology, antibodies source, measuring range, analytical sensitivity and reference range. 2. Intra and inter-assays precision, linearity and standard addition-all analytical parameters were performed according to known guidelines. 3. A scoring system which evaluated each test according to: a) r – depicted from the correlation coefficient, b) Slope and intercept of the correlation, c) Concordance with the clinical interpretation.
Results: According to these parameters we scientifically scored the five instruments. The final score has taken into account also financial and technical support issues.
Conclusions: The ARCHITECT was the chosen platform where we have already implemented the tests for CA 125 and CA15-3 with very good analytical and clinical performance.

P-80 Standardization

Immunoassays for determination of individual forms of SCCA in serum

Hall C, Dahlén U, Röijer E, and Nilsson Olle
CanAg Diagnostics AB, SE-414 55 Göteborg, Sweden

Aims: To develop immunoassays for specific determination of the individual serological forms of SCCA's in order to explore the molecular composition of SCCA released in different forms of disease.
Methods: Antibodies for free and complexed forms of SCCA1, SCCA2, and Pan SCCA MAb were established and used for development of immunoassays.
Results: The pan-specific CanAg SCC EIA, targeting epitopes located in Exon 2 – 7, showed similar reactivity with SCCA1 and SCCA2. The technical and clinical validation showed excellent performance of the assay. The median for a healthy population of blood donors was 0,54 µg/L. The correlation coefficient of the SCC EIA versus Abbott SCC IMx was r= > 0.98. The CanAg SCCA2 EIA, targeting epitopes in exon 2-7 and 8 respectively, recognized both free and complexed SCCA2 with less than 1% cross reactivity with SCCA1.
Analyses of serum samples from different patient categories confirmed previous findings on increased release of SCCA in squamous cell carcinomas. It was further shown that the assay for total SCCA2 could detect forms of SCCA not recognised by the "Pan specific" assays CanAg SCC EIA or Abbott SCC IMx. An additional finding was that the relative distribution in serum of SCCA1 and SCCA2 varies between different benign and malignant conditions.
Conclusions: This finding may implicate that assays for the different forms of SCCA could be tailored for different clinical applications such as squamous cells carcinomas of the cervix, lung or head & neck, respectively.

P-81 Standardization

Multicenter evaluation of the ARCHITECT® CA19-9™$_{XR}$ assay

Olson James[1], Blankenstein M[2], Mitchell H[3], Roberts W[4], O'Morchoe S[1], Rosiere T[1], et al.
[1]Abbott Diagnostics Division, Abbott Park, IL; [2]VU University Medical Center, Amsterdam, The Netherlands; [3]Charing Cross Hospital, London, UK; [4]ARUP Laboratories, Salt Lake City, UT; [5]Abbott Diagnostics Division, Delkenheim, Germany; [6]Fujirebio Diagnostics Inc, Malvern, PA

Aims: The purpose of these studies was to evaluate the performance of the ARCHITECT CA19-9$_{XR}$ assay.
Methods: Evaluation studies for this assay were conducted at one U.S. and two European sites. The ARCHITECT CA19-9$_{XR}$ assay is a two-step, chemiluminescent immunoassay for the quantitative determination of 1116-NS-19-9 reactive determinants in human serum, to be used in conjunction with other clinical methods in the management of pancreatic cancer patients.
Results: Analytical sensitivity, at 95% confidence, was determined to be 1.06 U/mL for 12 runs. Total variability, using a 5-day NCCLS EP10-A2 protocol for controls, ranged from 5.9 to 8.3 %CV. In method comparison testing, Pearson correlation coefficients ranged from 1.00 vs. Bayer Centaur® and 0.96 for Cezanne Kryptor® to 0.79 vs. DPC Immulite® and 0.77 vs. Beckman Access DxI®. Slopes from Passing-Bablok analyses ranged from 0.98 to 2.16, depending on the sample ranges and assays compared. Concordance ranged from 97.0% with Centaur to 91.7% with Immulite and 90.9% with DxI.
Conclusions: ARCHITECT CA19-9$_{XR}$ has proven to be a convenient, sensitive and precise assay with an extended dynamic range (2 – 1200 U/mL) and good to excellent agreement with existing CA19-9 assays.

P-82 Standardization

Performance of ARCHITECT ® CA 19-9™$_{XR}$, an enhanced chemiluminescent microparticle assay for the ARCHITECT® system

Smith GA, Covert WE[1], O'Morchoe SB[2]
[1] Fujirebio Diagnostics Inc, Malvern, PA; [2] Abbott Diagnostics, Division, Abbott Park, IL

Aims: To assess the performance of the ARCHITECT CA 19-9$_{XR}$ assay.
Methods: The ARCHITECT CA 19-9$_{XR}$ assay is a chemiluminescent microparticle immunoassay for the quantitative determination of 1116-NS-19-9 reactive determinants. The assay is used in conjunction with other clinical methods in the management of pancreatic cancer. This two-step assay utilizes paramagnetic microparticles coated with monoclonal antibody 1116-NS-19-9, an acridinium labeled monoclonal antibody 1116-NS-19-9 conjugate and assay diluent. The resulting chemiluminescence is measured as relative light units (RLUs). The RLUs generated are directly proportional to the amount of 1116-NS-19-9 reactive determinants in the sample.
Results: Precision studies, using a 3 member serum-based panel, yielded total CV's ranging from 3.4 to 6.5%. The analytical sensitivity was <2.0 U/mL. Interference from endogenous substances and chemotherapeutic agents was 100 ± 12%. Dilution recovery averaged 105%, ranging from 98% to 117%. One hundred and sixty-five specimens within the assay dynamic range were analyzed on the ARCHITECT and the Fujirebio Diagnostics CA 19-9 RIA for the presence of CA 19-9. Analysis by Passing-Bablok linear regression yielded a slope of 1.03, an intercept of –3.16 and an r-value of 0.94.
Conclusions: An accurate, sensitive and precise CA 19-9 assay, with the advantage of an extended range, has been developed for the ARCHITECT instrument system.

P-83 Standardization

Abstract not submitted.

P-84 Standardization

Comparison of four different assays for determination of serum S-100B

Bonfrer JMG, Smit LHM[2,3], Korse CM[1]
[1]Department of Clinical Chemistry, [2]Department of Surgical Oncology, [3]Department of Medical Oncology, The Netherlands Cancer Institute – Antoni van Leeuwenhoek Hospital, Amsterdam, The Netherlands

Background: S-100B determination has been shown to be clinically useful in the management of melanoma patients. After the development of a test for determination of the isoforms S100-A1B and S100-BB in serum 100B), several sensitive assays for detection of serum have become available. We compared four S-100B assays, two automated (LIAISON®Sangtec®100 and Elecsys®S100) and two manual ones (Sangtec®100 ELI and CanAg S100EIA), with respect to clinical data, reference values and correlation.
Methods: In a total of 280 samples from 155 melanoma patients and 98 healthy individuals S-100B values were measured simultaneously with the different assays.
Results: The inter- and intraassay coefficients of variation were best for the automated assays. The functional sensitivity of both manual assays was 0.15 µg/L. Method comparison revealed satisfactory correlation coefficients of 0.9 or higher, but the slopes ranged from 0.29 to 3.36. Except for the Sangtec®100 ELISA, the linearity between the assays was acceptable. The overall sensitivity for melanoma ranged from 37% (Elecsys®S100) to 47% (LIAISON®Sangtec®100) and the sensitivity increased with stage. ROC curves showed the best accuracy for the LIAISON®Sangtec®100 assay.
Conclusions: All assays gave satisfactory results, but it is advisable to improve the performance of manual assays for better sensitivity. Agreement about an international reference standard is needed.

P-85 Hematology

Serum cytokine levels correlate with clinical parameters in Hodgkin's disease

Kowalska Maria[1], Kaminska J[1], Rysinska A[1], Tajer J[2], Walewski J[2]
[1]Dept. of Tumor Markers, [2]Lymphoma Dept, Cancer Centre and Institute of Oncology, Warsaw, Poland

Aims: The aim of this study was to analyze correlations between the levels of cytokines and clinicopathological features of the Hodgkin's disease.
Methods: The study comprised 61 patients with previously untreated HD. All tumors were histologically verified as HD. The staging was performed according to the Ann Arbor classification system. Patients who suffered from an unexplained fever (>38°C), night sweats or weight loss (>10% of body weight in 6 months) were considered to have B – symptoms. The levels of IL-1 , TNF , IL-6, IL-8, IL-10 and IL-1ra were measured by ELISA of R&D.
Results: The majority of cytokine concentrations were found elevated and only IL-1β fell within the normal range in most cases. Serum levels of IL-6, IL-10 and IL-1ra were increased in over 50% of patients. As assessed by the analysis of ROC curves, IL-6 and IL-10 measurements revealed the highest diagnostic sensitivity. The levels of IL-6 and IL-10 were significantly higher in younger patients, IL-10, IL-1ra and TNFα increased with clinical stage, IL-6, IL-10 and TNFα with B-symptoms present, IL-6 with massive mediastinal mass and IL-10 with the number of sites involved.
Conclusions: The increased levels of IL-10 that most frequently correlated with unfavorable clinicopathological features, seem to be associated with poor prognosis in HL.

P-86 Hematology

Simultaneous determination of biomarkers in human sera by multiplex immunoassay

Karlikova M, Topolcan O
Medical Faculty of Charles University, Pilsen, and Faculty Hospital in Pilsen, Czech Republic

Aims: The role of cytokines, chemokines and soluble adhesion molecules as biomarkers has been largely discussed and the methods for their measurement in various human body fluids have been investigated. It is known that these substances interact in a complex network within the immune system. Therefore, a simultaneous measurement of multiple biomarkers in one aliquot of sample represents an effective approach.
Methods: Multiplexed assays were developed that can quantify biomolecules in a small sample volume. One method of multiplexed analysis can be performed by capture of the biomolecules on an array of fluorescent microspheres for quantitation by flow cytometry. In our study we have investigated the performance characteristics of the simultaneous measurement of several cytokines or soluble adhesion molecules in human sera with the multiplex system Luminex.
Results: In the cytokine panel we measured IL-6, IL-8, IL-10 and VEGF. The lower limit of quantification for all assays was less than 10 pg/mL. In the panel of adhesion molecules, sICAM, sVCAM and tPAI were measured. The lower limit o quantification for all assays was 80 pg/mL for sICAM and sVCAM and 18 pg/mL for tPAI. The intraassay precision for all analytes was determined as the average of the variation coefficients from 12 values for two different concentrations of controls. The inter-assay precision was assessed as the average of the variation coefficients through two different assays (total of 36 control simplex). Our experimental values were very close or even lower than the reported values of the analytical kit producer, which means a very good precision of our measurements. Around 130 serum samples were analyzed for each panel.
Conclusion: The method has proven to be sensitive and precise with important savings on time and sample volume.

P-87 Hematology

Monoclonal antibodies and molecular biology in the diagnosis of lymphoproliferative disease: Our experience

Buda Francesco, Stimolo A, Bergamo O, Svenda G, D'Agnolo E, *Aragona P, **La Torre F
Med Oncology and Clin Research Laboratory, "City of Udine" Hospital.* Clin Research Laboratory and Micro-biology ASL n 6 FVG Region, Italy ,** Dept of Surgery and Medical Oncology University, Messina, Italy.

Aims: To evaluate monoclonal Ab and molecular biology assays in the diagnosis of hematological diseases.
Methods: 84 patients with a lyphoproliferative NHL-type pathology. The examined material consists in nodal tissue obtained during the definitive bioptical diagnostic research. For the phenotype-immunologic investigation, cryostat sections were set up to estimate the presence of heavy and light chains for Ig and a number of AbMo were used to estimate the differentiation antigens of T and B cells. For the genotype-immunologic investigation the DNA was extracted from tissue samples and analysed according to the standard procedure. The rearrangement of the T cell receptor was analysed using a specific probe for the constant region C 1 and C 2 after DNA digestion with ECO R1, BAM, HIND. The Ig genetic rearrangements analysis were examined using a specific probe for JH, regions of the heavy chains after digestion with BAM and HIND.
Results: The presence of specific monoclonal Igs an the lymphomatosis cells resulted in 73 examined samples; other 10 samples were identified as B origin for the presence of least 2 antigens (CD19, CD20, CD22) In all these cases the presence of B monoclonal population was shown with the rearrangement of the JH and in most cases the crossbreeding with a JH probe showed 1 or 2 bands in addiction to a germ-line. 8 cases were diagnosed as T-cell peripheral lymphoma CD1 negative, CD3 positive confirmed with a DNA analysis which showed the rearrangements of the T receptor. 3 more cases were considered as anaplastic lymphoma showing positive response k1, CD 30 Ab, and the DNA analysis showed a germ-line configuration of both the T R and the Igs.
Conclusions: The analysis carried out through Southern Blot for the Igs and the Tcr was a trustfull clonical indicator and the genomic investigation extremely important especially in those cases without definite results in histology and immuno-histochemistry.

P-88 Hematology

Nucleosomes predict early the response to induction therapy in patients with acute myeloid leukaemia

Mueller Susanne[1], Holdenrieder S[1], Stieber P[1], Haferlach T[2], Schalhorn A[2], Nagel D[1], Seidel D[1]
[1]Institute of Clinical Chemistry, [2]Internal Medicine III,
University Hospital Munich-Grosshadern, Munich, Germany

Background: Nucleosomes showed to predict early the response to chemotherapy in solid tumors.
Patients and methods: Here, nucleosomes were measured in sera of 25 patients with de novo and relapse acute myeloid leukemia during the first cycle of induction chemotherapy and were correlated with therapy efficacy. In addition thymidine kinase, lactate dehydrogenase and leukocytes were analyzed in parallel.
Results: According the criteria of the German AML Cooperative Group, 18 patients reached complete remission and 7 showed no remission.
Nucleosome concentrations decreased in almost all patients during the first week, in some cases after initial peaks. In overall analysis, nucleosome levels distinguished clearly between patients with complete remission and those with insufficient response (p=0.017). In detail, significantly higher concentrations were found at days 2 and 4 after start of chemotherapy (p=0.014, and 0.022, respectively). A tendency to higher levels in patients with complete response was also found for thymidine kinase, lactate dehydrogenase and leukocytes, however the difference did not reach the level of significance (p=0.542, p=0.260, and p=0.144, respectively)
Conclusion: Circulating nucleosomes are a valuable marker for the prediction of therapeutic efficacy in patients with acute myeloid leukaemia – already at the very initial phase of the treatment.

P-89 Urology

Reference range evaluation for free/total prostate specific antigen (Kryptor) in a population of 895 men prior to systematic transrectal ultrasound-guided prostate biopsy

Semjonow Axel[1], Kranz M[1], Füchtenkötter M[1], Oberpennig F[2], Bettendorf O[3], Eltze E[3], Grunow G[4], De Angelis G[5], Fobker M[5]

[1]Prostate Center, Dept. of Urology, Univ. Münster; [2]Dept. of Urology, Univ. Bonn; [3]Prostate Center, Institut of Pathology, Univ. Münster; [4]BRAHMS, Henningsdorf-Berlin; [5]Prostate Center, Dept. of Clin. Chemistry, Univ. Münster, Germany

Aims: Validation of the reference range of the Kryptor assay system for free (F) over total (T) PSA in a population of men prior to systematic transrectal ultrasound-guided prostate biopsy (Bx).

Methods: Serum samples of 895 men drawn before Bx were used to determine F- and T-PSA prospectively with two assay systems, Beckman-Coulter Hybritech Access (A) and Kryptor, Brahms (K). The results of Bx were used to validate the reference ranges of the assay K in comparison to assay A. T-PSA concentrations of all men ranged between 2 and 20 ng/ml as measured with assay K.

Results: 429 men had benign biopsies and 466 had prostate cancer (PCa). The areas under receiver operating characteristics curves (AUC) for T-PSA did not differ significantly 0.57 (95% CI: 0.54-0.61) and 0.57 (95% CI: 0.54-0.60) for assay A and K, respectively. In both assay systems F/T-PSA was superior to T-PSA ($p<0.001$). The AUCs for F/T-PSA were 0.67 (95% CI: 0.63-0.70) and 0.68 (95% CI: 0.65-0.71) (p=n.s.) for assay A and K, respectively. The F/T-PSA reference ranges correspond closely between the assay systems: 95% of all biopsy negative pts. show a F/T-PSA >7% in both assay systems.

Conclusions: Both assay systems perform similar with regard to T- and F/T-PSA and differentiate between Bx and PCa with the same accuracy applying the same cutoffs.

P-90 Immunolgy

A human chimeric immune receptor specific for CEA generated by using four kinds of genes of human origin

Shibaguchi Hirotomo[1,2], Huang J[1], Kuroki MO[1,2], Hachimine K[1], Zhao J[2], Kinugasa T[1,2], Kuroki MA[1,2]

[1]Department of Biochemistry, Fukuoka University School of Medicine; [2]Molecular Oncology Center, Fukuoka University, Fukuoka, Japan.

Aims: Recombinant chimeric immune receptor (CIR) with anti-CEA specificity can retarget grafted T cells to CEA-expressing tumors in an HLA-independent manner. To dissolve the immunogenicity of usual CIR in humans, we tried to generate a human CIR by using four kinds of genes of human-origin.

Methods: A single-chain variable fragmented (scFv) antibody gene was prepared from variable region genes of the C2-45 human MAb clone specific for CEA. The scFv gene was connected to the human CD8 hinge region, the human CD28 transmembrane and cytoplasmic domain, and the human CD3 intracellular domain genes. The resulting human CIR gene, designated *L45scFv-CIR*, was inserted into the pIRES expression vector and transfected into the Jurkat T cells.

Results: Flow cytometric analysis using rhodamine-labeled CEA confirmed the expression of the L45scFv-CIR protein on the Jurkat cells and its specific antigen binding activity.

Conclusions: This *L45scFv-CIR* gene, consisting of four genes of human-origin, may be a useful tool for eradication of CEA-expressing but HLA-downregulated tumor cells.

P-91 Immunolgy

Influence of peptide LDSYQC(acm)T - $AFP_{14\text{-}20}$ on the expression of surface lymphocytes receptors in allergic inflammation

Salmasy JM, Terentiev Alexander, Poryadin GV, Makarov TV, Moldogazieva NT, Kazimirsky AN
Department of Biochemistry and Department of Patophysiology, Russian State Medical University, Moscow, Russia

Aims: Study of changes in surface antigens on lymphocytes received from patients with bronchial asthma allows estimating the direction of peptide $AFP_{14\text{-}20}$ immunotrophic actions in cellular model with human lymphocytes activated by allergic inflammatory process.
Methods: Human lymphocytes were cultivated for 16 hours with synthetic peptide LDSYQC(acm)T - $AFP_{14\text{-}20}$ in final concentration of 10^{-8} M. The acm is the aceto amide methyl group protecting cysteine from spontaneous oxidation and preventing formation of peptides dimers. Surface lymphocytes receptors were determined by a method of indirect immune fluorescent microscopy. The study was carried out on a group of 8 patients whose lymphocytes were characterized with unspoiled expression of induction apoptosis activation receptor (CD95).
Results: During lymphocytes cultivation in presence of peptide $AFP_{14\text{-}20}$ the decrease expression of all investigated activation antigens, except for CD23 (CD25, CD71, CD54, CD95, HLA-DR), has been observed. Besides the decrease of antigen expression in the main lymphocytes populations: CD3, CD16, CD20 has been observed.
Conclusions: The studied peptide $AFP_{14\text{-}20}$ possesses a considerable immunotrophic effect. This peptide essentially suppresses the expression of main lymphocytes activation antigens, and thus suppresses the development of immune inflammation. These properties of $FP_{14\text{-}20}$ can be rather useful in the development of a new generation of anti-inflammatory drugs.

P-92 Immunolgy

Peptide LDSYQC(acm)T-$AFP_{14\text{-}20}$ is capable to increase lymphocytes apoptosis in inflammation

Kazimirsky AN, Salmasy JM, Alexandrova IA, Moldogazieva NT, Tagirova AC, Terentiev Alexander
Department of Biochemistry and Department of Patophysiology, Russian State Medical University, Moscow, Russia

Aims: Inflammatory process in severe allergic and autoimmune diseases is accompanied by progressive insufficiency of lymphocytes activation apoptosis. In case of severe and extended inflammation the insufficiency of activation apoptosis is considered to be compensated by the other kind of apoptosis - TNF-induced lymphocytes apoptosis. These suggestions determine the purpose of the present study, which includes the definition of apoptosis levels of lymphocytes activated by inflammatory processes under the influence of synthetic peptide $AFP_{14\text{-}20}$.
Methods: Peptide LDSYQC(acm)T - $AFP_{14\text{-}20}$ is obtained by a firm phase synthesis method. Human lymphocytes were cultivated for 16 hours with synthetic peptide $AFP_{14\text{-}20}$ in final concentration of 10^{-8}M. Activation antigens (Fas and FasL) on lymphocytes surface were determined by indirect immunefluoriscent method. Lymphocytes were preliminary treated with digitonine to increase the permeability of plasmatic and nuclear membranes and were colored with propidium iodide. Then the registration of lymphocytes apoptosis was carried out.
Results: In group of 6 patients with severe and extended allergic inflammation the number of lymphocytes expressed Fas and FasL receptors did not exceed 6 and 7 percent correspondently. Under $AFP_{14\text{-}20}$ influence the number of cells expressing these receptors increased in 2-3 times. The level of $CD95^{+}$-lymphocytes apoptosis increased from 25-30% to 60-70% under $AFP_{14\text{-}20}$ influence.
Conclusions: The studied peptide $AFP_{14\text{-}20}$ increases a apoptosis level in $CD95^{+}$-lymphocytes in case of its insufficiency.

PBI-1393 enhances Th1 cytokine production and CTL response against tumor cells

Allam Mustapha, Julien N, Penney C and Gagnon L
ProMetic BioSciences Inc., Montreal, Quebec, Canada

Background: It was previously shown that PBI-1393, N,N-Dimethylaminopurine pentoxycarbonyl D-arginine (formerly BCH-1393), increased CTLs in normal immune status and immunosuppressed mice and inhibited tumor outgrowth when given in combination with subtherapeutic doses of cytotoxic drugs (cytoxan, 5-fluorouracil and doxorubicin).
Aims: The purpose of this study is to confirm *in vitro* human CTL activation by PBI-1393 and to demonstrate that this low molecular weight drug enhances IL-2 and IFN-γ gene expression.
Materials and Methods: Generation of antigen specific CTLs against human prostate cancer cells (PC-3) was performed by stimulation of purified human Peripheral Blood Mononuclear Leukocytes (PBML) with tumor cell lysates alone or in combination with IL-2 or PBI-1393 at day 0 and 3. CTL activity was measured six days later. For T cell proliferation, PBML were stimulated with IL-2 or PBI-1393 for 3 days. Alamar blue was used to measure cell proliferation. Cytokine release was measured by ELISA and gene expression was analyzed by RT-PCR. IL-2 transcription factors and Erk1/2 activation were also analyzed.
Results: PBI-1393 enhanced *in vitro* activation of human CTLs against PC-3 and T cell proliferation. PBI-1393 increased Th1 type cytokine IL-2 and IFN-γ at protein and gene level. The enhancement of IL-2 gene expression by PBI-1393 is associated with c-fos and ERK1/2 activation.
Conclusions: PBI-1393 is a potent activator of human T cells and a modulator of Th1 type cytokines. These results suggest that PBI-1393 is a promising drug in immunotherapy against cancer.

P-94 Melanoma

Effect of lactoferrin formulated in liposomes on different cell lines

Trif Mihaela[1], Roseanu A[1], Chelu F[1] , Radu M[1], Prunescu P[2], Brewer J[3]
[1]Institute of Biochemistry, [2]Institute of Biology, Romanian Academy, Bucharest, Romania; [3]University of Glasgow, Department of Immunology, Glasgow, UK

Aims: The aim of this study was to establish the liposomal formulation suitable to entrap and deliver lactoferrin (Lf) efficiently to melanoma B16-F1 cells and bone marrow derived dendritic cells (DCs). Lf is an iron-binding glycoprotein with potent antitumoral and anti-inflammatory activity.
Methods: Liposome ability to deliver Lf in melanoma B16-F1 cells was monitored using radioactively labeled protein. Fluorescence microscopy studies were used to detect liposomal systems into the cytoplasm of cells. Flow cytometric analyses of DCs surface markers expression was performed. The cytolines production was assessed in DCs cultures supernatants by capture ELISA.
Results: Liposomal formulations with different surface charge had greater capacity to deliver Lf to B16-F1 cells compared to free protein. Lf induced changes on the cells growth and morphology. Investigating the liposome stability in the presence of serum we have found that positive liposomes were more stable than neutral and negative ones. Liposome entrapped-Lf modified the degree of expression of DCs surface markers, MHC II, CD 40, and CD 86, and the cytokines level in DCs cultures when compared to exposure to free protein.
Conclusions: Our results showed that liposomes could be used as efficient carriers for controlled delivery of Lf into call and are encouraging for therapeutic use.

P-95 Melanoma

Humoral immune response of mice and humans to xenogenic vaccination with living melanoma cells growing in PAAG capsule.

Sologub Vladimir, Koromyslova I, Kotelevits A, Severin S
Moscow Res. Inst. Of Medical Ecology, Russia

Aims: We have shown protective effect of vaccination with living human melanoma cells (Sk-Mel-1) against mouse melanoma (B-16) and suggested to use B-16 as a vaccine against human melanoma. It was important to detect antibodies against shared mouse/human antigens in the sera of animals and human volunteers before and after xenogenic anti-melanoma vaccination.
Methods: Indirect ELISA with anti-IgG horse radish peroxidase conjugates was applied to determine titers of antibodies against: whole melanoma cells (human and mouse), GM3 ganglioside, S100B antigen and AFPR. Mouse monoclonal antibodies were produced after whole cell xenogenic immunization by standard fusion.
Results: Significant increases of antibodies were detected in sera of vaccinated mice and volunteers against xenogenic and some allogenic melanoma cells, and against GM3 and S100B but not against AFPR. Four of twenty-one mouse Mab´s appeared to be specific to S100B and three were specific to GM3. Five Mab´s were significantly therapeutic for B-16 tumor bearing mice – one anti-GM3 and two anti S100B.
Conclusions: Serum antibodies are important marker of existence and level of immunity. In our case, we have shown specificity of xenovaccination by living tumor cells encapsulated into PAAG. Future application of these and another melanoma specific antigens for antibody detection would be very interesting for monitoring of vaccinations and determination of "protective" level of immunity against melanoma.

P-96 Melanoma

S100 (A1B+BB), S100A1B and S100BB as markers for prediction of survival and relapse during long-term follow up of malignant melanoma

Bolander Ä[1], Bergqvist M[1], Brattström D[1], Larsson A[2], Ullenhag G[1], Hesselius P[1], Wagenius G[1], Einarsson R[13]
[1]Department of Oncology; [2]Department of Medical Sciences, Uppsala University Hospital, Uppsala; [3]CanAg Diagnostics, Gothenburg, Sweden

Aims: The combination of S100 markers may give additive information concerning increased risk of relapse and death in malignant melanoma patients.Protein S100B belongs to the S100/calmodulin/troponin C superfamily of EF-hand calcium binding proteins. S100 proteins (20 members) constitute a multigenic family of low molecular weight proteins (10-12 kDa). S100B and S100A1 form either homodimers (S100BB) or heterodimers (S100A1B).
Methods: CanAg S100, S100A1B and S100BB - are solid-phase, 2-step enzyme immunoassays based on monoclonal antibodies specific for different epitopes expressed on S100B. S100 technical performance; high sensitivity (detection limit <10 ng/L), intra-assay CV 1.3-2.5%, inter-assay CV 1.5-2.5%) and measuring range 10-3500 ng/L. S100A1B and S100BB have a detection limit of <10 ng/L and <30 ng/L, respectively and the analytical imprecision for S100A1B and S100BB is below 4%.
Results: An upper reference limit of 90 ng/L was obtained for S100 in 269 healthy individuals. 198 patients (UICC stage I and II) with cutaneous malignant melanoma were analysed after primary surgery and monitored up to 7.5 years or until time to death. Relapse was recored in 28 patients and death in 16 patients. S100 serum concentration was in the range 20-8330 ng/L, for S100A1B 0-7267 ng/L and for S100BB 0-2575 ng/L. Increased level of S100, S100A1B and S100BB reflected worse overall survival (statistically significant) applying the decision levels 150, 50 and 50 ng/L, respectively. Increased levels of S100 and S100BB correlated with the increased risk of relapse (p=0.02) and (p=0.03), but this was not found for S100A1B (p=0.7).
Conclusions: Individual patients show differencesc applying the S100 assays. S100A1B and S100BB might give further information in patients with different types of malignant melanoma and as early indicator for progressive disease.

P-97 Melanoma

S-100 in eye and cutaneus melanoma

Jaunalksne Inta, Donina S*, Sarkova G, Nikiforenko J, Pried te V, Nuke I*, et al.
VAS Paula Stradina KUS, Clinical Immunology Center; *Latvian Oncology Center, Riga, Latvia

Aims: Protein S-100 is used as a marker in skin melanoma, but there are no data regarding eye melanoma, therefore we decided to check eye melanoma patients for s-100 protein.
Methods: We determined S100 protein by ELISA, CanAg, Sweden and since 2005. we used the chemiluminiscence method (Elecsys 2010, Roche). We analysed 10 donors to check the used cut-off level and 21 patients with eye melanoma.The donors' average age was 36 years, the eye melanoma patients' average age was 47 y., in this group were 7 men and 14 women. 57 cutaneous malignant melanoma patients at various stages of disease were examined under follow-up examination. 38 patients had no evidence of disease (NED), 12 patients had lymph node metastasis and 7 patients had visceral or/and distant skin metastasis. Diagnosis was confirmed by histological examination of the operation material.
Results: The volunteers had mean eye S-100 values below the companies' recommended S100 cutoff level. 32% of eye melanoma patients had elevated S-100 levels. In cutaneous melanoma patients with no evidence of disease the mean S-100 level was 55.7+/-28.2pg/ml; patients with lymph node metastasis had 96.3+/-36.6, but in the patients' group with visceral or/and distant skin metastasis we obtained S-100 levels from 70.4 to 8042pg/ml.
Conclusions: S-100 protein is more sensitive in cutaneous melanoma patients, and their highly elevated values are indicators for more unfavourable prognosis. Our results for eye melanoma patients are preliminary and need further enlargement of the patients' group.

P-98 Melanoma

Abstract not submitted.

P-99 Thyroid

The use of tissue tumor markers in thyroid nodule diagnosis - recommendations from large multi-centric studies

Ludvíková Marie[1], Topolcan O[2], Kholová I[3], Rydlová M[4] and Holubec L jr[2]
[1]Department of Pathology; [2]Nuclear Medicine, Medical Faculty Hospital, Plzen; [4]Department of Pathology, Medical Social Faculty, Ostrava, Czech Republic; [3]A.I.Virtanen Institute for Molecular Sciences, University of Kuopio, Finland

Differential diagnosis of thyroid nodules is a problem in routine cytological and histopathological practice. Many tumor markers have been studied so far, but for routine use to differentiate among non-neoplastic, benign and malignant nodules of follicular cell origin, these markers are not specific and sensitive enough.
Aims and Methods: To summarize tissue tumor markers in thyroid pathology and their practical implications in differential diagnosis. Presentation will focus predominantly on the following panel of markers: dipeptidyl peptidase IV (DPP IV), galectin-3, human thyreoperoxidase (hTPO), CD 56, thyroid transcription factor 1 (TTF1), proliferative markers MIB-1 and topoisomerase II- , that we thoroughly studied in large series of cytological and histopathological specimens.
Results and conclusions: Available tissue tumor markers can be used routinely in differential diagnosis of thyroid tumors only as auxiliary tools and the morphological diagnostic criteria remain as a golden standard. The „magic biomarker" to segregate thyroid disorders into malignant and benign remains to be discovered.

The work was supported by the fund MSM-VZ 0021620819

P-100 Thyroid

Thyroglobulin detection in fine-needle aspirates of cervical lymph nodes: a technique for the diagnosis of metastatic papillary thyroid cancer.

Cunha Nuno[1], Curado F[1], Rodrigues F[2], Monteiro S[2], Campos B[2], Valido F[1]
[1]Seviço de Patologia Clínic, [2]Seviço de Endocrinologia,
IPOFG-Centro Regional de Oncologia de Coimbra-Portugal

Fine needle aspiration cytology is frequently used for differential diagnosis of neck masses of unknown origin. Inconclusive and even false negative results are not uncommon.
Aims: Evaluation the utility of thyroglobulin measurement in fine-needle aspirates (FNA-Tg) of cervical lymph nodes (CLN), as a method of surveillance of low risk thyroid cancer.
Methods: An ultrasound-guided fine-needle aspiration was done in 33 patients with suspicious lymph nodes, to obtain material for cytology and Tg measurement. The Tg was measured in the needle washout, using an immunometric chemioluminescent assay, with a functional sensitivity of 0.9 ng/ml.
Results: 17 patients had high values of FNA-Tg (11.1-55000 ng/ml). FNA-cytology showed metastasis of papillary thyroid cancer in 11 cases, reactive lymphadenitis in one case and the remaining 5 were non diagnostic (3 of these cases were cystic CLN). All underwent cervical lymphadenectomy. Histological examination confirmed the diagnosis of metastatic lymphadenopathies initially suggested by FNA-Tg high values. 16 patients had undetectable FNA-Tg (<0.5 ng/ml) with negative FNA-cytology and therefore no further treatment was undertaken.
Conclusions: Our data suggested that this simple and fast technique has higher sensitivity than cytology, especially when the CLN display cystic features, and thus may be very useful in the diagnosis of metastatic papillary thyroid cancer.

P-101 CEA

Production of single chain variable fragments (scFv) in Pichia pastoris

Marianne Nordlund, Warren DJ and Paus E
Central Laboratory, The Norwegian Radium Hospital HF, Oslo, Norway

Aims: NCA-2, a C-terminal truncated form of CEA, predominates in meconium and is present in sera from adult cancer patients. Single-chain variable antibody fragments (scFv) specific for NCA-2 were selected from a phage-display library and produced in *E. coli* with relatively low yields (1.5 mg /L). The aim of this study was to produce scFv in the yeast *Pichia pastoris* with either a multi-copy expression system with a methanol inducible *AOX1*-promoter or a constitutive expression system with a *GAP*-promoter. The yeast cells can be grown to very high cell densities and have strong promoters and efficient secretion.
Methods: Production of scFv was performed in the *P. pastoris* expression system. scFv were cloned into the pPIC9K inducible cloning vector for selection of multi-copy expression or pGAPZα for constitutive expression. The single-chain fragment was purified by nickel-affinity chromatography and labelled with Eu-chelate.
Results: Multi-copy expression resulted in four-fold increases in yield compared to *E. coli* (4.6 mg/L). Maximal production however, was obtained with constitutive expression (17 mg/L). The Eu-labelled antibody fragment worked well in the immunofluorometric assay for NCA-2.
Conclusions: Single-chain variable antibody fragments can be efficiently expressed in *P. pastoris* and used as a tracer-antibody in a two-site assay for NCA-2.

P-102 Thyroid

sIL-2R as a marker for laryngeal cancer

Gross M[1], Hochwald E[1], Eliashar R[1], Kalickman I[2], Barak V[2]
Dept of ENT, Head and Neck Surgery[1], Immunology Lab for Tumor Diagnosis[2], Hadassah-Hebrew University Medical Center, Jerusalem, Israel

Aims: To test soluble IL-2 receptor levels (sIL-2R) as a potential marker for assessing treatment response and prognosis in laryngeal cancer.
Methods: We have assessed 60 larynx cancer patients pre and 28 post-surgery. In addition, 20 healthy age-and sex-matched controls were included. Correlations of sIL-2R levels(medians) to grade, stage, lymph node involvement, and pathology were performed. Levels of sIL-2R were evaluated by an ELISA assay.
Results: Serum levels (medians) of sIL-2R after surgery were higher than before (963 ± 65 vs. 797± 108; p=0.05). Higher levels were found in T4 patients compared to T1, T2 and T3 patients (1073 ± 122 vs. 671 ± 52; p=0.02). It is interesting to note that nodal disease did not cause significant change in sIL-2R levels compared to negative nodal disease (1013 ± 187 vs. 886 ± 73; p=0.4). In poorly differentiated cancer, levels of sIL-2R were significantly higher (1377 ± 55 vs. 777± 37; p=0.001) than in well differentiated cancers .According to ROC analysis, sIL-2R levels distinguish by 90% between laryngeal cancer patients and normal controls at a cut off point of 533 U/mL.
Conclusions: Higher sIL-2R levels correlate to a higher grade and to poorly differentiated laryngeal cancer. sIL-2R levels may distinguish between laryngeal cancer patients and healthy individuals. A better survival rate is attributed to patients with higher levels of sIL-2R.

P-103 CEA

Prognostic markers for head and neck cancer

Hochwald[1] E, Gross[1] M, Eliashar[1] R, Kalickman[2] I, Barak[2] V
Dept of ENT, Head and Neck Surgery[1], Immunology Lab for Tumour Diagnosis[2], Hadassah-Hebrew University Medical Center, Jerusalem, Israel

Aims: To test SCC, TPS and CYFRA 21-1 as potential markers for evaluating treatment response and prognosis in head and neck cancer patients (pts), larynx cancer and oral cavity cancer.
Methods: We have assessed 60 larynx cancer pts. pre and 28 post-surgery, 29 oral cavity cancer pts. pre and 23 post-surgery. In addition, 20 healthy age-and sex-matched controls were included. Correlations of marker levels (medians) to stage, lymph node involvement, grade and pathology were performed. All 3 markers were evaluated by ELISA assays.
Results: Serum levels (medians) of all 3 markers were higher and decreased after surgery in patients with larynx cancer. (SCC-1.64 ± 0.3 to 0.7 ± 0.08, p=0.02; TPS - 77.5 ± 8.4 to 53.7 ± 6.1 ns; CYFRA 21-1- 1.54 ± 0.3 to 1.11 ± 0.17, ns). In oral cavity cancer pts. SCC levels decreased significantly (1.67 ± 0.2 to 0.99 ± 0.19, p=0.05). Higher levels of all 3 markers were found in T3, T4 pts. as compared to T1, T2 pts.(SCC - 1.93 ± 0.9 to 0.88 ± 0.17, p=0.07; TPS - 77.3 ± 9.9 to 61.7 ± 6.7, p=0.012; CYFRA 21-1 - 1.33 ± 0.2 to 0.89 ± 0.2, ns). Significantly higher levels of CYFRA 21-1 were found in larynx cancer pts than in oral cavity cancer pts. Node positive pts. had significantly higher TPS levels as compared to node negative pts. (76± 0.91 vs 44 ± 1.17, p=0.02). and T3,T4 pts had also significantly higher levels than T1,T2 pts (76=0.91 vs 50=1.54, p= 0.012) All parameters were placed in a multivariate analysis. TPS and CYFRA 21-1 were found to be independent prognosticators.
Conclusions: TPS, CYFRA 21-1 and SCC serum levels can serve as markers of head and neck cancer. Of all 3 markers TPS proved to be the most sensitive predictor of advanced disease and poor prognosis, correlating to stage and nodes. Overall survival was significantly correlated to high levels of TPS-55% pts alive after 2 y and 40 % after 5y. vs 90% pts alive after5y, for those having low TPS levels pre surgery.

P-104 ENT

Expression of P53 and BCL-2 proteins in primary laryngeal carcinoma cells cultures after incubation with cisplatin

Klatka Janusz[1], Paduch R [2], Po arowski P[3]
[1]Dept. of Otolaryngology, Med University, Lublin; [2]Dept. of Virology and Immunology, Maria Curie-Skłodowska University, Lublin; [3]Dept. of Clinical Immunology, Medical University, Lublin, Poland

Primary culture of laryngeal carcinoma cells in vitro, opens new perspectives for biological and clinical studies. Particular interest is focused on testing viability of tumour cells and in consequence evaluating the effectiveness of cytostatic drugs to select suitable treatment.
Aims: to evaluate the expression of P53 and BCL-2 proteins in primary laryngeal carcinoma cell cultures after incubation with cisplatin.
Methods: The expression of P53 and BCL-2 was evaluated in 19 primary laryngeal carcinoma cell cultures, which were grown from tissue samples obtained after laryngectomy of 19 patients. The expression of the protein, in primary cell cultures before and after 24 hours of incubation with cisplatin in dose 0.5 μg/ml was measured using monoclonal antybodies and laser scaning cytometry (LSC).
Results: Statistically significant increase in P53 expression in primary laryngeal carcinoma cells cultures after incubation with cisplatin was observed ($p<0,05$). Statistically significant correlation between P53 and BCL-2 expression in primary laryngeal carcinoma cells cultures after incubation with cisplatin was observed ($p<0,005$).
Conclusions: The estimation of cisplatin effect on P53 and BCL-2 proteins expression in primary laryngeal carcinoma cells cultures may be helpful to explain how selected cytotoxic drugs suppress the proliferative capacity of those cells. Such information may be useful in studies of the mechanisms and effectiveness of new anti-tumour drugs.

P-105 ENT

Predicting radiosensitivity: correlation of nitric oxide synthase and GST-pi expression in human oral cancers

Vesper Benjamin J[1], Hammer ND[1], Bentz BG[2], Haines GK[3], Radosevich JA[1]
[1]Center for Molecular Biology of Oral Diseases, College of Dentistry, University of Illinois-Chicago, Chicago, IL, USA, [2]Dept. of Otolaryngology Head & Neck Surgery, University of Utah, Salt Lake City, UT, USA, [3]Dept. of Pathology, Northwestern University, Chicago, IL, USA

Aims: Patients with oral tumors are frequently treated with radiation, a method that kills tumor cells via free radical production. Response to radiation varies, however, and there is a need to develop molecular markers which predict radiation sensitivity. Human oral tumors are known to express high levels of functional Nitric Oxide Synthase (NOS) and Glutathione-S-transferase-pi (GST-pi), enzymes responsible for the production of nitric oxide (NO) and the corresponding protective mechanism, respectively. Previous studies have shown that high expression of NOS/GST-pi correlates with a worse outcome, and we here explore if a correlation exists between the over-expression of NOS/GST-pi and radiosensitivity.
Methods: Four human oral squamous cell carcinoma cell lines were exposed to 0-20 Gy of gamma irradiation, and the relative sensitivity was determined using the MTT assay. Expression levels of NOS/GST-pi were determined using standard immunohistochemical methods.
Results: Sensitivity to radiation directly correlated with increased degree of NOS/GST-pi expression.
Conclusions: These results suggest that radiation sensitivity may be predicted based upon the degree of NOS/GST-pi over-expression; and although high NO-producing tumors might respond better to treatment, this response may actually predict a poor overall patient outcome.

P-106 ENT

Glutathione-S-Transferase-pi (GST-pi) is over-expressed in radiation-resistant human squamous cell laryngeal tumors

Radosevich James A[1], Waltonen JD[2], Altman KW[3], Bentz BG[4], Haines GK[5]
[1]Center for Molecular Biology of Oral Diseases, College of Dentistry, University of Illinois-Chicago, Chicago, IL, USA, [2]Dept. of Otolaryngology Head & Neck Surgery, Northwestern University, Chicago, IL, USA, [3]Mt. Sinai School of Medicine, Dept. of Otolaryngology, New York, NY, USA [4]Dept. of Otolaryngology Head & Neck Surgery, University of Utah, Salt Lake City, UT, USA, [5]Dept. of Pathology, Northwestern University, Chicago, IL, USA

Aims: Glutathione-S-transferase-pi (GST-pi), an enzyme found to be overexpressed in head and neck squamous cell carcinomas (SCC), is believed to protect tumor cells from radiation-induced oxidative injury. We investigated the expression of GST-pi in advanced laryngeal SCC, some of which had been previously treated with radiation therapy.
Methods: Ten patients underwent total laryngectomy for SCC of the larynx. These tumors were immunostained to the expression of GST-pi using standard immunohistochemical methods. Patient charts were reviewed, with focus on the pre-operative treatment.
Results: The expression of GST-pi varied from 1+ to 4+ in both focal and diffuse staining patterns. The staining was stronger in tumors that had been previously treated with radiation therapy than those that had not.
Conclusion: Tumors that persisted or recurred despite treatment with radiation therapy demonstrated increased expression of GST-pi, suggesting that the expression of this enzyme may serve as a predictor of response to radiation therapy in treating SCC of the larynx.

P-107 ENT

Tumor markers in squamous cell carcinoma of the larynx

Eleftheriadou A[1], Lambrini Kyriou[2], Pappas Z[1], Chalastras T[1], Ferekidis E[3], Kandiloros D[3]
[1]Department of Otolaryngology, G. Gennimatas Hospital, Athens;
[2]Department of Biochemistry, Evangelismos Hospital, Athens;
[3]Department of Otolaryngology, University of Athens, Ippokration Hospital, Athens, Greece

Aims: The identification of a reliable circulating tumor marker in laryngeal cancer could assist in early diagnosis and monitoring response to therapy.
The aim of this study was to investigate the effectiveness of the serum tumor markers CYFRA 21-1, TPA –M, CA 72-4, SCCA and CEA.
Methods: Serum levels of CYFRA 21-1, TPA–M, CA 72-4, SCCA and CEA were measured in 60 patients with a histologically proven SCC of the larynx before and after treatment and in 60 healthy subjects, as controls. We tried to evaluate the sensitivity and specificity of these tumor markers and to correlate the levels with tumor staging, grading or performance status. .
Results: The study showed that none of the above markers presented satisfactory specificity and sensitivity. In comparison with the rest markers, only high levels of TPA-M slightly correlated presenting an association with low-moderate differentiation of the tumor.
Conclusions: All the tumor markers that were studied have significant limitations in the early diagnosis of laryngeal cancer.

P-108 AFP

Interaction of AFP– derived peptides with 17 -estradiol: a molecular dynamics simulation study

Moldogazieva NT, Terentiev Alexander, Antonov MYu, Shaitan KV
Dept. of Biochemistry, Russian State Medical University, Moscow, Dept. of Bioengineering, Moscow State University, Russia

Aims: The study was theoretical computer analysis of interaction of AFP-derived peptides with 17 -estradiol. There were tree peptides with affinity to 17 -estradiol: rat AFP (RAFP) ELIDLTGKMVSIAST (424-438) and two human AFP (HAFP) – ELMAITRKMAATAAT (428-442) and AADIIIGHLCIRHEM (458-472).
Methods: Computer analysis with molecular dynamic simulation study.
Results: Affinity calculations from the pairwise distances values showed preferences for binding of, predominantly, hydrophobic amino acids to the estrogen. They are Glu-428, Leu-429, Ile-432, Arg-434, Met-436, Ala-440, Ala-441 and Thr-442 residues of high-affinity HAFP-derived peptide and Ala-458, Ala-459, Asp-460, Ile-461, Ile-462, His-465 and Arg-469 residues of low-affinity HAFP-derived peptide. In RAFP-derived peptide the following amino acid residues were preferable for interaction: Glu-424, Asp-427, Lys-432, Met-433, Ile-435, Ala-436 and Ser-437. The calculations demonstrate that four estrogen molecules in the system are more preferable than one molecule for stability of the complex. Besides, it was shown that two or three estrogen molecules are able to simultaneously interact with one peptide molecule. It is probable that variable conformational changes in the peptides are caused by different amount of hormone in the system and explain different affinity of E2 to the peptide.
Conclusions: This data is in agreement with reported experimental results for estrogen-binding sites of the AFPs. Our results support the data and give further suggestions regarding amino acids which are essential for estrogen binding.

P-109 AFP

Abstract not submitted.

P-110 AFP

Abstract not submitted.

P-111 AFP

Analysis of phylogenetic relationship between alpha-fetoprotein (AFP) and serum albumin (SA) on the basis of pairwise sequence alignment

Terentiev Alexander, Moldogazieva NT, Tatarinov YuS
Department of Biochemistry, Russian State Medical University, Moscow, Russia

Aims: Earlier the most conservation of unprocessed sequences of human AFP and SA was reported (Terentiev A.A., ISOBM 2004, p.77). In this work we aimed to analyze phylogenetic relationships between AFP and SA in species based upon pairwise sequence alignment procedure.
Methods: From Swiss-Prot and TrEMBL data bases we derived the protein sequences for six mammalian species and one bird (chick) and saved them in FASTA format. We generalized pairwise alignments of processed (mature) and unprocessed (immature) sequences of the proteins using ClustalW (version 1.82) program exploiting default parameters.
Results: Identity degrees between the pairs of AFP and SA unprocessed sequences decrease from human (40%) towards chick (39%), dog (38%), pig (37%), horse (35%), mouse (34%) and rat (32%). Total similarities between the pairs of the sequences calculated taking into account amount of conservative substitutions decrease from chick (64.2%) to human (63.9%), dog (63.8%), horse (61.8%), pig (61.7%), mouse (61.3%) and rat (58.6%). Identities between the processed (mature) sequences of AFP and SA are higher in chick (41%) than in human (40%), however decrease in the same manner towards horse, mouse and rat. Total similarities between mature sequences decrease in the same manner as identities.
Conclusions: In this paper we demonstrate that the pair of chick mature AFP and SA sequences is the most conservative and this is confirmed by calculation of total similarities between mature and immature sequences.

P-112 New Markers

An ELISA assay for detection and quantification of heparanase

Shafat I[1], Nadir Y[1], Nakhoul F[2], Barak V[3], Ilan N[1] , Vlodavsky Israel[1]

[1]Vascular and Tumor Biology Research Center , The Bruce Rappaport Faculty of Medicine, Haifa, Israel; [2]Nephrology Division, Rambam Medical Center; [3]Department of Oncology, Hadassah-Hebrew University Medical Center, Jerusalem, Israel

Aims: Development of a sensitive ELISA assay for determination and quantification of human heparanase.
Results: The assay preferentially detects the 8+50 kDa active heparanase heterodimer at concentrations as low as 250 pg/ml, and is suitable for quantification of heparanase in tissue extracts, urine, pleural effusions, plasma and serum. A 4-5 fold increase in heparanase levels was found in urine samples of leukemia patients vs. urine collected from healthy donors ($p = 0.05$). Increased (~3 fold) levels of urinary heparanase were also detected in patients with diabetic nephropathy.
Conclusions: The ability to quantify heparanase levels in plasma, urine and body fluids provides a basis for a large scale screen evaluating heparanase levels as a diagnostic and prognostic marker for several disorders such as cancer and diabetes.

P-113 New Markers

Antibody pair selection for development of a new TIMP-1 immunoassay

Sørensen, Nanna M[1], Christensen IJ[2], Jensen V[1], Brünner N[1], Nielsen HJ[2], Dowell B[3], Davis G[3]
[1]Department of Veterinary Pathobiology, Royal Veterinary and Agricultural University, Denmark
[2] Department of Surgical Gastroenterology, Hvidovre Hospital, Denmark
[3] Abbott Diagnostics Division, Abbott Laboratories, Abbott Park, IL, USA

Aims: Develop a new double monoclonal antibody (mAb) sandwich immunoassay for **T**issue **I**nhibitor of **M**etalloproteinases-1 (TIMP-1) in order to achieve better resolution of non-cancer and cancer specimens.
Methods: Chemiluminescence immunoassay techniques were used to screen 240 combinations of TIMP-1 mAbs for their ability to sandwich with each other, and to further evaluate the sandwiching antibody pairs. Plasma specimens from persons undergoing endoscopy with no indication of colorectal cancer and colorectal cancer patients were measured with 5 mAb pair immunoassays, and compared with measurements obtained in a reference polyclonal antibody /mAb total TIMP-1 ELISA that had previously demonstrated ability to resolve donors and cancer specimens.
Results: Free TIMP-1, TIMP-1 in complex with matrix metalloproteinase-9 (MMP-9) or Pro-MMP-9 were tested in the 152 mAb pair combinations that yielded calibrations. Five mab pair immunoassays were selected and evaluated for their ability to discriminate non-cancerdonors and colorectal cancer specimens. Four of the immunoassays resolved the donor and cancer specimens as well as the reference ELISA.
Conclusions: One mAb pair was selected for further development of a new TIMP-1 immunoassay based on strength of signal/dose response, specificity for various TIMP-1 complexes, mAb affinities, and ability to resolve donor and cancer specimens.

P-114 New Markers

Comparison of biochemical markers of bone turnover in breast and prostate cancer patients with metastatic bone disease

Lyubimova Nina V, Pashkov MN, Kochergina NV
Russian N.N.Blokhin Cancer Research Center, Moscow; N.N.Burdenko Medical Academy, Voronezh, Russia.

Aims: The evaluation of the utility of bone markers tartrate-resistant acid phosphatase 5b (TRAP 5b) and bone alkaline phosphatase (BAP) in breast and prostate cancer patients with bone metastases.
Methods: Bone resorption (TRAP 5b) and bone formation (BAP) markers were studied in 178 breast and 102 prostate cancer patients with and without bone involvement. Serum levels of TRAP 5b and BAP were measured using the enzyme immunoassay Bone TRAP («Medac Diagnostika») and BAP EIA kit («BCM Diagnostics»).
Results: Pre-treatment levels of TRAP 5b were significantly higher in breast and prostate cancer patients with bone metastases than in healthy women and men and patients without clinical signs of metastatic spread to the bone. TRAP 5b elevation was associated with the extent of metastatic bone disease in breast carcinoma patients (R=0.529; p=0.00001). Serum levels of TRAP 5b gradually decreased in patients with positive clinical response to Bondronat therapy; in patients with progression of disease serial TRAP 5b values increased progressively. Diagnostic sensitivity of TRAP 5b for breast and prostate cancer patients was 78.9% and 66.7% (specificity 92.8% and 96.2%), and the sensitivity of BAP was 60.0% and 84.4% (specificity – 92.6% and 89.5%), respectively.
Conclusions: Measurement of TRAP 5b may be used in the detection of bone metastases and for the evaluation of bisphosphonate treatment effects on bone in cancer patients.

P-115 New Markers

SCCA, SCCA1, SCCA2 in healthy persons and patients with benign disease

Kulpa Jan Kanty, Rychlik Urszula, Wójcik Ewa, Reinfuss Krzysztof, Misiak Ewa
Center of Oncology – M.Skłodowska-Curie Memorial Institute, Cracow Division, Poland

Aim: SCCA1 and SCCA2 are subfractions (neutral and acidic) of SCCA found in normal squamous epithelia, and are strongly expressed in squamous cancer cells. SCCA are accepted as serological markers for squamous cell cancer of uterine cervix, lung, head and neck. Most clinical studies of serum SCCA have been performed using Abbott's IMx system. Newly developed immunoassays specific for SCCA, SCCA1 and SCCA2 are now available. The aim of study was the estimation of SCCA and its subfractions distribution in healthy subjects and patients with benign disease and also in respect to CRP level as inflammation factor.
Methods: The determinations of SCCA, SCCA1 and SCCA2 using ELISA CanAg reagent kits were performed in group of 129 healthy persons and 53 with benign disease.
Results: In patients with benign disease were observed significantly higher SCCA1 and SCCA2 than in healthy people at similar SCCA levels in both groups. In healthy people weak but significant differences in SCCA, SCCA1, and SCCA2 levels were found in respect to gender; female showed lower levels of SCCA as well as SCCA1 and SCCA2. Elder people presented tendency to higher SCCA and its both subfractions levels than younger people, but differences between groups separated in respect to age were not significant.
Conclusions: Gender but also inflammation status influence the SCC levels.

P-116 THERAPY

The correlation between meeting physical needs of children during chemotherapy and the mother's knowledge

Namnabati, M
Faculty of Nursing, Isfahan, Iran

Aims: Special needs are developed by children treated for cancer which should be met by health care teams, physicians and parents, the most influential being the mothers, if they are well equipped to deal with the required needs in this regard . Accordingly, this study was made to survey the correlation between meeting physical needs of children during chemotheraphy and mother's knowledge.
Methods: This is a correlation study. The data collection tool was a questionnaire organized in three parts. It was completed by 32 mothers whose children were receiving chemotherapy in Seidoshohada Hospital in Isfahan
Results: Findings revealed that most mothers (56.2%) had no appreciable knowledge about the physical needs of their children and a majority of them (68.8%) did not how to treat these needs properly. Alhough, 42.8% of the samples had sufficient understanding, only 31.2% of them met their children's physical needs correctly. No meaningful correlation was found between the knowledge about physical needs and the way they are met (X = 0.33 df=1).
Conclusions: The results indicated that the research hypothesis is refuted with 95% assurance; and therefore it is incorrect to say that mothers with higher knowledge meet their children's physical needs better than those with lower knowledge because some of them were found aware of their children's needs nevertheless, they did not treat them properly.

P-117 THERAPY

Positron Emission Tomography versus tumor markers in oncology

Nekulová Mirka, Bol ák K, Šimí ková M, Frgala T, Pilný R, Valík D
MOÚ, Brno, Czech Rep.

Aims: Comparison of validity of diagnostic procedures in relation to disease recurrence.Positron Emission Tomography (PET) represents the most dynamically evolving diagnostic method of late, employed in oncology, neurology, and cardiology. It detects accumulation patterns of 2-deoxy-2-[18F]fluor-D-glucose in the fast growing tumor cells. The indications for PET in oncology are: assessment of the biological character of the tumor, early detection of relapse, and therapeutic effect evaluation.
Methods: Tumor markers (TM) were determined in patient serum via immunoanalytical methods: ß-hCG, CA 15-3, CA 125, CA 19-9, PSA, ß2M (AxSYM Abbott), CEA, AFP, NSE, CYFRA 21-1 (Elecsys ROCHE), SCCA (IMx Abbott). TM measurements were evaluated in a total of 624 patients repeatedly examined with PET. The condition of TM measurement within a month before or after each individual PET scan was kept in 233 patients, out of which 31 patients were selected with discrepancies between the PET and TM results.
Results: In 19 cases the TM values were falsely negative (60 %). In 12 patients (14 %) increasing TM values signalized a possible relapse and prompted a PET examination. An evidential CA 125 increase in one case led to diagnosis of duplicate breast carcinoma in an ovarian cancer patient.
Conclusions: The combination of PET with TM appears profitable. Especially in ovarian and breast cancer patients increasing TM levels can warrant a PET examination to detect relapse or tumor duplicity.
The study was supported by Scientific and Research Scheme MZ000209805 and IGA NR 8342-3/2005

P-118 THERAPY

The clinical value of FDG-PET in patients with increased levels of serum S-100B and negative conventional work-up

L.H.M. Smit[1,2], E.F.I. Comans[3], J.M.G. Bonfrer[4], R.A. Valdés Olmos[5], G.C. de Gast[2], O.E. Nieweg[1]
[1]Department of Surgical Oncology, [2]Department of Medical Oncology, [4]Department of Clinical Chemistry, [5]Department of Nuclear Medicine, The Netherlands Cancer Institute – Antoni van Leeuwenhoek Hospital, Amsterdam, [3]Department of Nuclear Medicine, VU Medical Center Amsterdam, The Netherlands

Aims: The S-100B protein is increasingly being used as tumor marker in patients with melanoma. Its clinical utility has been described in determining prognosis, treatment monitoring and for early diagnosis of recurrence. PET is another relative new method used in melanoma patients to diagnose metastatic disease, to monitor treatment and to provide additional information when conventional imaging techniques are not conclusive. We examined the additional value of PET in melanoma patients with repeatedly elevated serum S-100B values in whom other imaging techniques (MRI of the brain, CT of thorax and abdomen and scintigraphy of the bone) did not reveal a melanoma recurrence.
Patients and methods: Twenty-eight patients with elevated serum S-100B values but no signs of melanoma recurrence following the aforementioned imaging techniques were studied with PET.
Results: A positive PET-scan was obtained in fifteen patients, thirteen had negative PET-imaging. The sensitivity and specificity of PET to reveal melanoma recurrence were 100% and 82% respectively. PET led to additional treatment in ten of eleven patients with a true-positive scan: chemotherapy in three and surgery in seven. Four of these surgically treated patients are alive without recurrence after a median of sixteen months.
Conclusions: The sensitivity of PET in patients with an elevated S-100 and normal conventional imaging techniques is 100% and the specificity is 82%. The PET findings result in a change in the management in 36% of the patients. An elevated serum S-100B in melanoma patients, who are considered to be disease-free and have no established recurrence site after conventional imaging techniques, is a reason to contemplate FDG-PET-scanning.

P-119 SCCA

Squamous cell carcinoma associated antigen on the Architect® system evaluated

Sandri Maria Teresa[1], Chieregatti I.[2], Dolci A.[2], Bellati P.[3], Barberis M.[2]
[1]Laboratory Medicine Unit, European Institute of Oncology, Milan, Italy;
[2]Pathology Department, H MultiMedica, Milan, Italy;
[3]Abbott Diagnostics, Rome, Italy

Aims: squamous cell carcinoma associated antigen (SCC) is a 48 kD glycoprotein widely used as serum tumor marker in monitoring the response to therapy of squamous cell carcinomas. We evaluated two-step chemiluminescent immunoassay for SCC determination on Architect system.
Methods: shortened 5-days NCCLS protocol EP10-A was applied in two Italian sites on Architect automated system (Abbott Diagnostics) based on paramagnetic microparticle chemiluminescent technology. The two-step immunoassay utilizes two anti-SCC monoclonal antibodies (MAb), first MAb coated with the magnetic microparticles, the second one labelled with acridinium. Dynamic range of Architect SCC assay is 0.1 – 70 µg/L and the throughput 200 tests/hour. For analytical correlation we selected IMx (Abbott Diagnostics) as reference system
Results: total imprecision of low (2.0±0.1 µg/L), medium (10.3±0.3 µg/L) and high (49.4±1.8 µg/L) controls is 4.9, 2.7 and 3.7 CV% respectively, assay analytical sensitivity <0.05 µg/L. Correlation testing with the IMx, performed on 100 samples (range 0.1-67.9 µg/L), shows a Pearson correlation coefficient of 0.997, a slope of 1.43 and an intercept of 0.11, with an outlier result (4.7 and 1.0 µg/L on different systems).
Conclusions: SCC automated immunoassay on Architect system shows high sensitivity, low imprecision and, in terms of accuracy, very high association to IMx with a systematic proportional overestimation of the data.

P-120 SCCA

SCCA, SCCA1 and SCCA2 in cervical cancer patients

Kulpa Jan[1], Rychlik U[1], Jakubowicz J[1], Einarsson R[3], Rusiecka G[2], Sedlaczek P[2]
[1]Center of Oncology, Cracow Division, [2]Medical Academy, Wrocław, Poland, [3]CanAg AB, Sweden

Aim: Squamous cell carcinoma antigen was first isolated from uterine cervix squamous cell carcinoma and now is generally accepted as marker of choice for this malignancy. Acid and neutral subfractions of this protein were separated. Most clinical studies with serum SCCA have been performed using the IMx system (Abbott Diagnostics). The aim of study was to compare sensitivity and specificity of serum levels of SCCA, SCCA1, SCCA2 and SCCA IMx in uterine cervical cancer patients.
Methods: The determinations of SCCA, SCCA1, SCCA2 (CanAg AB) and SCCA IMx (Abbott Diagnostics) were performed in 137 uterine cervix cancer patients in different stages of disease before treatment and in reference group of 37 healthy women.
Results: SCCA, SCCA1, and SCCA2, levels and SCCA2/SCCA1 ratio as well as SCCA IMx concentrations were significantly higher in uterine cervix cancer patients in comparison with reference group. Analysis of ROC curves revealed significantly higher sensitivity of SCCA1 than of remaining forms of antigen (AUC: 0.80, 0.86, 0,77, 0.68 and – 0.77 for SCCA, SCCA1, SCCA2, SCCA2/SCCA1 and SCCA IMx respectively), at lack of significant differences in diagnostic sensitivity between SCCA and SCCA IMx, SCCA and SCCA2, SCCA IMx and SCCA2. The group of cervical cancer patients showed significant relationship between clinical stage of disease and tumor markers concentrations.
Conclusions: SCCA1 seems to optimize biochemical diagnostics of cervical cancer.

P-121 CA 125

Analytical performance of CA 125 mucin tumor marker on ARCHITECT i2000 analyzer

Bellati Paola*, Martinasso G., Priolo G., Betteto S., Becattini M., Mengozzi G., Baldi C.
Laboratory of Clinical Chemistry "Baldi e Riberi", Azienda Sanitaria Ospedaliera San Giovanni Battista, Torino (Italy), *Abbott Diagnostics

Aim: CA 125 is defined by using the OC 125 monoclonal antibody; high serum CA 125 levels are mainly associated with serous ovarian cancers.
Methods:We evaluated performances of second-generation CA 125 assay on Architect i2000 analyzer (Abbott Laboratories), and compared with those of Axsym (Abbott Laboratories) and Kryptor (BRAHMS) systems.
Results:Within-run CV (n=10) was 1.5% and 3.2% at 46.2 and 110.8 U/mL, respectively. Between-day imprecision (n=20) was 5.6% and 4.4% on the same pools and with two reagent lots. According to Passing and Bablok regression, and to Altman and Bland comparison, a slope=1.21, an intercept = -2.45 and a mean bias=36.1 was found between Architect and Kryptor on 119 consecutive routine samples. The comparison between Architect and Axsym yielded a slope=1.46, an intercept=6.35 and a mean bias=85.44 on a series of 167 consecutive specimens. Discrepancies among tested methods appeared at least partially improved when looking at CA 125 concentrations below 500 U/mL, even if the same threshold limit is suggested by manufacturers.
Conclusions:These data suggest that differences in CA 125 values among methods may arise mainly when facing with higher concentrations and should be taken into account if results from different laboratories are to be evaluated.